If you could change your entire name to just 1 letter, what would you choose? →

If you love this
Coke or Pepsi?
book, then check
out more

books for you & your friends.

Coke or Pepsi?

More Coke or Pepsi?

Coke or Pepsi? 3

The Ultimate Coke or Pepsi?

Coke or Pepsi? GIRL!

Coke or Pepsi? GIRL! Diary

My Best Year

coke-or-pepsi.com

coke

OR

pepsi?

UNLIMITeD!

What do you really know about your friends?

SCHOLASTIC INC.
New York Toronto London Auckland
Sydney Mexico City New Delhi Hong Kong

coke

OR

pepsi?

UNLIMITED!

Written and designed by
Mickey & Cheryl Gill

ISBN 978-0-545-34041-0

12 11 10 9 8 7 6 5 4 3 2 1   11 12 13 14 15 16/0

Printed in China   53

First Scholastic printing, January 2011

Pass this book around to all of your **friends**.
Each **friend** has a chance to answer
some pretty cool **questions**.
See what **you** have in common.
Find out what makes you **different**.
Some **answers** might even shock **you!**

Answer a set of
questions and
pass it back.

⊙ Cherry Coke
◯ Pepsi Wild Cherry?

R u a pouter?
◯ Oh yeah
⊙ Sometimes ◯ Nah

What do you think of when
you see the word - noodles?

2 sticky
things u luv?

Would u rather be
⊙ respected for doing
the right thing
◯ liked by everyone
for being fun?

⊙ M&M's
◯ Skittles?

If u could teleport somewhere for 1 day, where would you go?

BEST PART OF A SANDWICH?

Good hula hooper?

Would you really want to be a QUEEN?

POPSICLE?
CREAMSICLE?
FUDGSICLE?

Grossest thing in your fridge?

Would you rather have 3 eyes OR 4 arms?

If you could be any age for one year, what age would you pick?

Write down another word, sentence or really short story.

Name

noodles _____

bumblebees _____

HAUNTED HOUSE _____

flip-flops _____

paws _____

fist bump _____

yellow _____

fairy _____

fortune cookies _____

rock band _____

Follow me to your locker
at coke-or-pepsi.com!

Find more questions and free stuff in your personal locker at
coke-or-pepsi.com/locker. Your secret combination is 8-21-43.

I have a doppelganger
my friends say she looks just like me
should I try to find her?

1. Your last name (in pig Latin)? _____

2. Have a doppelganger in town (person who looks like you)? ○ Yes ○ No

3. Worst thing you've ever found in your food? _____ in _____.

4. Most annoying fashion trend? _____

5. How do you feel about purple? _____

6. Are you a pouter? ○ Oh yeah ○ Sometimes ○ Nah

7. What makes you tense? _____

8. Coolest thing about your family? _____

9. Weirdest thing about your family? _____

10. Snort when you laugh? ○ Yes ○ Sometimes ○ No

11. Do you make up songs? ○ No ○ Yes R they any good? ○ Yes ○ No

12. Yummiest thing in your fridge right now? _____

13. Grossest thing in your fridge right now? _____

14. ○ Talking ○ Texting on phone?

15. What would be your superhero name? _____

16. Fave famous athlete? _____

17. How many monogrammed items do you own? _____

18. Best street food? ○ Hot dogs ○ Candied nuts ○ Crepes ○ Pretzels

19. What could you write a book about? _____

20. Most interesting person you've ever met? _____

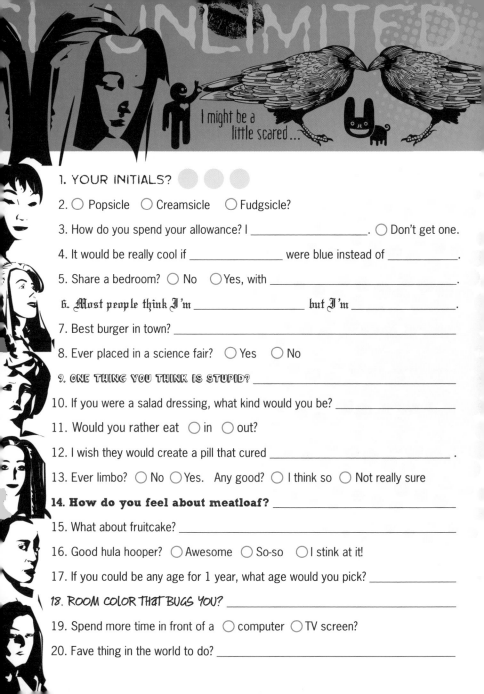

I might be a little scared...

1. YOUR INITIALS? ● ● ●

2. ○ Popsicle ○ Creamsicle ○ Fudgsicle?

3. How do you spend your allowance? I _____. ○ Don't get one.

4. It would be really cool if _____ were blue instead of _____.

5. Share a bedroom? ○ No ○ Yes, with _____.

6. Most people think J'm _____ but J'm _____.

7. Best burger in town? _____

8. Ever placed in a science fair? ○ Yes ○ No

9. ONE THING YOU THINK IS STUPID? _____

10. If you were a salad dressing, what kind would you be? _____

11. Would you rather eat ○ in ○ out?

12. I wish they would create a pill that cured _____ .

13. Ever limbo? ○ No ○ Yes. Any good? ○ I think so ○ Not really sure

14. **How do you feel about meatloaf?** _____

15. What about fruitcake? _____

16. Good hula hooper? ○ Awesome ○ So-so ○ I stink at it!

17. If you could be any age for 1 year, what age would you pick? _____

18. ROOM COLOR THAT BUGS YOU? _____

19. Spend more time in front of a ○ computer ○ TV screen?

20. Fave thing in the world to do? _____

Name . . . .

1. First name with letters mixed up . . . .

2. ○ Lime ○ Lemon ○ Lemon-lime?

3. Ever had a treehouse ? ○ Yes ○ No

4. Do u wear green? ○ No ○ Yes. Look good in it? ○ Yes ○ Dunno

5. Fave green veggie? . . . .

6. ○ Chartreuse ○ Grass green ○ Forest green?

7. Talked with a parrot? ○ No ○ Yes. What did it say? . . . .

8. Ever golfed? ○ No ○ Just goofy golf ○ Yes

9. Ever found a four-leaf clover? ○ Yes ○ No

10. Most green ($) you've had in your pocket? . . . .

11. Would you try green eggs and ham? ◯ Sure ◯ No way!

12. ◯ Spearmint ◯ Peppermint?

13. Believe in little green men? ◯ Yes! ◯ No, aliens don't exist.

14. Someone you know with green eyes? . . . .

15. Have any Irish in you? ◯ No ◯ Don't know ◯ Yes, ...

16. Like the movie with the Emerald City? ◯ Yes ◯ No, witch is scary!

17. Something that made you green with envy? . . . .

18. ◯ Green ◯ Red apples?

19. Write down the first green thing you see. . . . .

20. What 3 wishes would u ask of a leprechaun? . . . .

GET AIR

UNLIMITED TRAVEL

Would you mind having wings
if it meant you could fly?

1. First name upside down? _____

2. Chew on the ends of pencils or pens? ◯ Yes ◯ No

3. Something you've done that ur friends haven't? _____

4. What sound makes u laugh? _____

5. Like hot sauce? ◯ Luv it! ◯ No

6. Last subject you Googled? _____

7. Something u want to know about the future? _____

8. Do/Did u have Barbie dolls? ◯ No ◯ Yes. Which kind? _____

9. What's on ur nightstand or next to ur bed? _____

10. Something you quit? _____

11. Have a fave Disney princess? ◯ No ◯ Yes, _____.

12. Want to go to college? ◯ No ◯ Yes. Where? _____

13. What makes you sneeze? _____

14. Taste the difference between Coke and Pepsi? ◯ Absolutely ◯ Not really

15. Fave soap scent? _____

16. Last thing you borrowed? _____

17. Like Scrabble? ◯ Yes ◯ No

18. How 'bout Monopoly? ◯ Yes ◯ No

19. If u could live 1 day of ur life over, which would u choose? _____

20. COOLEST CAR YOU'VE BEEN IN? _____

I would fly straight to the moon.

1. LAST NAME? _____

2. Ever swallowed a non-food item? ○ No ○ Yes, _____.

3. ○ **Speakers** ○ **Headphones** ○ **Ear buds?**

4. Last song you sang out loud? _____

5. Would u mind having wings if it meant u could fly? ○ No ○ Yes

6. What do you put ketchup on? _____

7. HOW 'bOUT MUSTaRD? _____

8. Prefer to ○ take ○ be in a photograph?

9. Fave carnival game? _____

10. Tend to blame ○ yourself ○ others ○ a little of both?

11. Best part of a sandwich? _____

12. What's your current mood? _____

13. Fave four-legged creature? _____ Y? _____

14. ○ Fresh fruit ○ Fruit-flavored candy?

15. Last fight I had was about _____

16. Sneakiest place you've ever hidden? _____

17. **Would you like to be cloned?** ○ **Oh yeah** ○ **No way**

18. Fave kind of cheese? _____

19. What does your mouse pad look like? _____

20. ○ Daredevil ○ Scaredy pants?

WOULD U RATHER...

Name

have a spy ○ camera ○ listening device?

be ○ respected for doing the right thing ○ liked for being fun?

○ work really hard and make millions ○ win millions in a contest?

○ sleep in a hammock every night ○ sit in a wooden chair every day?

hang out ○ 1 time with a really cool celebrity ○ for a month with a guy you like?

always have ○ a stain on your shirt ○ something stuck in your front teeth?

have a lifetime of ○ bad hair ○ "I don't like any of my clothes!" days?

be a ○ cat with a litter box ○ dog that has to be taken out?

○ have a cold for 6 months ○ be cold for 6 months?

have the ability to ○ breathe underwater ○ go without sleep?

○ make new friends each year ○ keep your same friends you have now forever?

have ○ 3 eyes ○ 4 arms?

live without ○ salt ○ sugar?

have to wear ○ jeans to work out ○ a formal gown to the movie theater?

always have to wear cowboy ○ boots ○ hat?

whatdoyouthinkof

when you see or hear these words ...

Write down another word, sentence or really short story.

Name ______

POPCORN ______

stars ______

winter ______

texting ______

pirate ______

ELEVATOR ______

castle ______

BOYS ______

furry ______

pebbles ______

red

1. Name you wish you had? _____

2. Ever tried Red Hot candies? ○ No ○ Yes

3. ○ Red ○ Pink roses?

4. Look good in red? ○ Not really ○ Some shades ○ Yes

5. Redhead you know? _____

6. ○ Apples ○ Cherries ○ Strawberries?

7. ○ Red lipstick ○ Pink lip gloss ○ Neither?

8. ○ Red ○ Black ○ Refried beans and rice?

9. Which movie star rocks the red carpet? _____

10. ○ Cherry Coke ○ Pepsi Wild Cherry?

rouge
rojo
rosso

11. Which is cooler ... red ○ dress ○ shoes ○ bag?

12. Something red you would not part with? _____

13. Fave character in ruby red slippers movie? _____

14. ○ Red velvet ○ Chocolate ○ Vanilla cake?

15. Valentine's Day is ○ so overrated ○ OK, I guess ○ so sweet.

16. How'd u get your last bad sunburn? _____

17. ○ Red ○ Black raspberries?

18. Turn red when you are really mad? ○ YES! ○ No

19. How 'bout when you're embarrassed? ○ Oh yeah ○ No

20. ○ Tomato ○ Cream sauce on pasta?

Ever seen a
shooting star?

1. **NICKNAME?** _____

2. ○ Sunflower seeds   ○ Peanuts   ○ Granola?

3. Height? ▢ ▢

4. Shoe size? ▢

5. How long have you lived in the house you're in? _____

6. ○ Confetti   ○ Silly string?

7. What do you say when someone sneezes? _____

8. **Kind of cell phone u have or want?** _____

9. Know what ur name means?   ○ No   ○ Yes, _____ .

10. Fave love song? _____

11. ○ Cheetos   ○ Doritos   ○ Fritos   ○ Tostitos   ○ None of them?

12. **Question u would ask the President?** _____

13. Comforter pattern & color? _____

14. Trait ur parents love about u? _____

15. Trait of yours that bugs ur parents? _____

16. ○ **Rock wall**   ○ **Mountain climbing?**

17. Something u always take with u when u leave the house? _____

18. What makes you fall asleep? _____

19. Oldest thing in your wardrobe? _____ from _____

20. Seen a shooting star? ○ Yes ○ No   Meteor shower? ○ Yes ○ No

I wished I could be a superstar!

1. First name without vowels? _____

2. 3-D movies ○ are really cool ○ make me dizzy.

3. Any exciting news to share? ○ Nope ○ Yep, _____.

4. Fave fair food? ○ Funnel cakes ○ Fried candy bar ○ Sausages ○ Shaved ice

5. I cheer myself up by _____

6. Graffiti is ○ a really cool art form ○ tacky ○ illegal!

7. Shove things under ur bed so ur room looks clean? ○ Oh yeah ○ Uh no

8. Unsolved mystery in ur life? ○ No ○ Yes, _____.

9. ○ Sit-down dinner ○ Eat on the run?

10. COOKIE(S) ○ aND MiLK ○ aND CREAM iCE CREAM ○ DOUGH?

11. Idea for a new reality show? ○ No ○ Yes, _____.

12. Meet anyone new this week? ○ No ○ Yes, _____.

13. Caught a snowflake on your tongue? ○ Yes ○ No

14. States you've lived in? _____

15. Chicken tenders & ○ honey mustard ○ barbeque ○ other _____?

16. Spell well? ○ Yes ○ I'm average ○ No

17. if U were invited to a costume ball, who would U go as? _____

18. ○ Green ○ Black olives ○ Neither, gross!

19. Sat on a rooftop? ○ Yes ○ No

20. FAVE THING TO SLURP THRU A STRAW? _____

Would you really want to be a queen?

1. First name (spelled backwards)? ⬭

2. Playing with a ○ kitten ○ puppy ○ guinea pig is the most fun.

3. **WOULD YOU REALLY WANT TO BE A QUEEN?** ○ **ABSOLUTELY!** ○ **NO WAY!**

4. Most expensive thing you've broken? _____

5. Nails on a chalkboard? ○ AHHH! ○ Doesn't bother me.

6. ○ Love(d) ○ Hate(d) dodgeball?

7. If u could teleport somewhere for 1 day, where would you go? _____

8. **Wear/Wore braces?** ○ **Yes** ○ **No**

9. Like to go barefoot ○ whenever I can ○ sometimes ○ never!

10. Most important thing about you? _____

11. **EVER STEPPED ON A NAIL?** ○ **YES** ○ **NEVER**

12. Look good in hats? ○ No ○ Yes ○ Eh, maybe a few.

13. Last game you won? _____

14. Last game you lost? _____

15. **Double dipping is** ○ **so gross** ○ **not THAT big of a deal.**

16. Ever had food poisoning? ○ Yes, from _____. ○ No

17. Something you've never tried? _____

18. Make any interesting sounds? __ No __Yes, I _____.

19. Popular song you love to hate? _____

20. **Ever been hit by a ball?** ○ *No* ○ *Yes, I* _____.

Absolutely!

Power

(_____) 1. What do most people call you?

2. Wear watch on your ◯ **right** ◯ **left wrist?**

3. Can you go to bed hungry? ◯ Yes ◯ No, gotta have something.

4. Last craft you did? _____

5. Ever been in trouble for talking too much? ◯ Yep ◯ Nah

6. Ever been labeled "shy"? ◯ Not hardly ◯ A few times ◯ Always!

7. Participated in a staring contest? ◯ No ◯ Yes. Did you win? ◯ Yes ◯ No

8. Fave kind of socks? _____

9. Arm wrestled? ◯ **Yes** ◯ **No**

10. Thumb wrestled? ◯ Yes ◯ No

11. "For real" wrestled? ◯ No way ◯ Uh, yeah

12. Best thing about the last day of school? _____

13. Worst thing about the last day of school? _____

14. Know a lot of useless trivia? ◯ **Yes** ◯ **No, not really.**

15. Which color is scarier? ◯ Red ◯ Black

16. ◯ Sweet ◯ Sour pickles?

17. BEST FRO-YO IN TOWN? _____

18. Gone backstage at a concert? ◯ No ◯ Yes, I met _____ .

19. ◯ Corn on the cob ◯ Loose corn niblets?

20. Fave Wii game? _____

BLUE

1. Name _____

2. What makes you blue? _____

3. Look good in blue? ● Yes ● No

4. Two blue things in your bedroom? _____

5. Someone you know with blue eyes? _____

6. Blueberry ● pancakes ● pie ● smoothie ● muffin?

7. ● Bluebirds ● Blue flowers?

8. ● Baby ● Navy ● Aqua blue?

9. Favorite blue jeans brand? _____

10. ● Fly the blue sky ● Sail the blue seas?

BLUE

11. Seen the ocean? ⬤ No ⬤ Yes, I've been to _____.

12. ⭕ *Little Mermaid* ⭕ *Finding Nemo?*

13. ⭕ Submarine ⭕ Submarine sandwich?

14. ⭕ Ocean bottom ⭕ Outer space?

15. I would love to take a cruise to _____.

16. Think SpongeBob will ever get his license? ⭕ Yeah ⭕ Nah

17. ⭕ Crab legs ⭕ Crabcake ⭕ Krabby patties?

18. Owned a fish besides a goldfish? ⭕ No ⭕ Yes, a _____.

19. Like calamari? ⭕ Yum! ⭕ Yuck! ⭕ Whatamari?

20. Fave water activity?

If you could go back 24 hours, what would u change?

unlimited possibilities...

1. Middle name? _____

2. IF U COULD GO BACK 24 HOURS, WHAT WOULD U CHANGE? _____

3. Buffets are ○ so much fun ○ germy and gross.

4. Last song you danced to? _____

5. MOVIE THEATER PREVIEWS ARE ○ ANNOYING AND LONG ○ EXCITING.

6. Coolest old person u know? _____

7. Had anything stolen? ○ No ○ Yes, my _____

8. Most difficult thing you've done? _____

9. Air ○ guitar ○ drums?

10. If u could change ur entire name to one letter, which would u choose? ▢

11. Tallest person you know? _____

12. Ever fainted? ○ No ○ Yes, I _____

13. Own a tiara? ○ No ○ Of course

14. ○ Chili ○ Veggie chili ○ Neither?

15. Old song you really like? _____

16. SHOOK OR KICKED A VENDING MACHINE? ○ YES ○ NO, IT'S DANGEROUS!

17. Something you love about where u live? _____

18. Something you can't stand about it? _____

19. Care what people think of u? ○ Yeah ○ Depends who it is ○ Nah

20. ○ Karate chopping Styrofoam ○ Popping bubble wrap is more fun!

1. Name? _____

2. Other names for you ur parents considered? _____

3. **What r u doing?** _____

4. What were u doing this time last year? _____

5. 2nd toe longer than your big toe? ○ Yes ○ No

6. ○ Wal-Mart ○ Target ○ Other _____?

7. I was a ○ good ○ mean ○ hyper ○ weird little kid.

8. **name of your very first teacher?** _____

9. Did your first teacher like you? ○ Yes ○ No ○ I don't remember

10. Pick change up off the ground? ○ Yes ○ No

11. ***Sleep with your bedroom door*** ○ **open** ○ **closed?**

12. ○ Love thunderstorms ○ Lightning freaks me out!

13. ○ I don't want to get married. ○ I would like to be married by age _____.

14. Crying in front of people ○ doesn't bother ○ embarrasses me.

15. Fave symbol, logo, or icon? _____

16. Get motion sickness? ○ Yes ○ No

17. ○ **Lemonade** ○ **Pink lemonade?**

18. ○ M&M's ○ Skittles?

19. Is your family "huggy"? ○ Yep! ○ Not really

20. **FASTEST SPEED YOU'VE GONE AT IN A CAR?** [____]

two...

1. names you go by? _____

2. people who know you best? _____

3. sweets that go great together? _____

4. things you avoid? _____

5. objects in your backpack or bag? _____

6. things you've climbed? _____

7. places you've jumped from? _____

8. people or things that make u LOL? _____

9. things you've lost? _____

10. things that give u the creeps? _____

11. reasons that make u run fast? _____

12. things you wish existed? _____

13. foods you'd like to eat every day? _____

14. jobs you'd never do? _____

15. activities u do fast? _____

16. activities that take u forever? _____

17. reasons u stay awake @ night? _____

18. sticky things you love? _____

19. things u don't like to do in public? _____

20. things u don't like to do alone? _____

whatdoyouthinkof

when you see or hear these words ...

Write down another word, sentence or really short story.

Name

noodles _____

bumblebees _____

HAUNTED HOUSE _____

flip-flops _____

paws _____

fist bump _____

yellow _____

fairy _____

fortune cookies _____

rock band _____

Follow me to your locker
at coke-or-pepsi.com!

Find more questions and free stuff in your personal locker at
coke-or-pepsi.com/locker. Your secret combination is 3-17-28.

I have a doppelganger
my friends say she looks just like me
should I try to find her?

1. Your last name (in pig Latin)? _____

2. Have a doppelganger in town (person who looks like you)? ○ Yes ○ No

3. Worst thing you've ever found in your food? _____ in _____.

4. Most annoying fashion trend? _____

5. How do you feel about purple? _____

6. Are you a pouter? ○ **Oh yeah** ○ **Sometimes** ○ **Nah**

7. What makes you tense? _____

8. Coolest thing about your family? _____

9. Weirdest thing about your family? _____

10. Snort when you laugh? ○ **Yes** ○ **Sometimes** ○ **No**

11. Do you make up songs? ○ No ○ Yes R they any good? ○ Yes ○ No

12. Yummiest thing in your fridge right now? _____

13. Grossest thing in your fridge right now? _____

14. ○ **Talking** ○ **Texting on phone?**

15. What would be your superhero name? _____

16. Fave famous athlete? _____

17. How many monogrammed items do you own? _____

18. Best street food? ○ Hot dogs ○ Candied nuts ○ Crepes ○ Pretzels

19. What could you write a book about? _____

20. Most interesting person you've ever met? _____

I might be a little scared...

1. YOUR INITIALS? ⬤ ⬤ ⬤

2. ○ Popsicle ○ Creamsicle ○ Fudgsicle?

3. How do you spend your allowance? I _____. ○ Don't get one.

4. It would be really cool if _____ were blue instead of _____.

5. Share a bedroom? ○ No ○ Yes, with _____.

6. 𝕸𝖔𝖘𝖙 𝖕𝖊𝖔𝖕𝖑𝖊 𝖙𝖍𝖎𝖓𝖐 𝕵'𝖒 _____ 𝖇𝖚𝖙 𝕵'𝖒 _____.

7. Best burger in town? _____

8. Ever placed in a science fair? ○ Yes ○ No

9. 𝗢𝗡𝗘 𝗧𝗛𝗜𝗡𝗚 𝗬𝗢𝗨 𝗧𝗛𝗜𝗡𝗞 𝗜𝗦 𝗦𝗧𝗨𝗣𝗜𝗗? _____

10. If you were a salad dressing, what kind would you be? _____

11. Would you rather eat ○ in ○ out?

12. I wish they would create a pill that cured _____ .

13. Ever limbo? ○ No ○ Yes. Any good? ○ I think so ○ Not really sure

14. **How do you feel about meatloaf?** _____

15. What about fruitcake? _____

16. Good hula hooper? ○ Awesome ○ So-so ○ I stink at it!

17. If you could be any age for 1 year, what age would you pick? _____

18. *ROOM COLOR THAT BUGS YOU?* _____

19. Spend more time in front of a ○ computer ○ TV screen?

20. Fave thing in the world to do? _____

Name . . . .

1. First name with letters mixed up . . . .

2. ◯ Lime ◯ Lemon ◯ Lemon-lime?

3. Ever had a treehouse ? ◯ Yes ◉ No

4. Do u wear green? ◯ No ◯ Yes. Look good in it? ◯ Yes ◯ Dunno

5. Fave green veggie? . . . .

6. ◯ Chartreuse ◯ Grass green ◯ Forest green?

7. Talked with a parrot? ◉ No ◯ Yes. What did it say? . . . .

8. Ever golfed? ◯ No ◉ Just goofy golf ◯ Yes

9. Ever found a four-leaf clover? ◉ Yes ◯ No

10. Most green ($) you've had in your pocket? . . . .

11. Would you try green eggs and ham? ◯ Sure ◯ No way!

12. ◯ Spearmint ◯ Peppermint?

13. Believe in little green men? ◯ Yes! ◯ No, aliens don't exist.

14. Someone you know with green eyes? . . . .

15. Have any Irish in you? ◯ No ◯ Don't know ◯ Yes, ...

16. Like the movie with the Emerald City? ◯ Yes ◯ No, witch is scary!

17. Something that made you green with envy? . . . .

18. ◯ Green ◯ Red apples?

19. Write down the first green thing you see. . . . .

20. What 3 wishes would u ask of a leprechaun? . . . .

**Would you mind having wings
if it meant you could fly?**

1. First name upside down? _____

2. Chew on the ends of pencils or pens? ○ Yes ○ No

3. Something you've done that ur friends haven't? _____

4. **What sound makes u laugh?** _____

5. Like hot sauce? ○ Luv it! ○ No

6. Last subject you Googled? _____

7. Something u want to know about the future? _____

8. Do/Did u have Barbie dolls? ○ No ○ Yes. Which kind? _____

9. What's on ur nightstand or next to ur bed? _____

10. **Something you quit?** _____

11. Have a fave Disney princess? ○ No ○ Yes, _____.

12. Want to go to college? ○ No ○ Yes. Where? _____

13. **What makes you sneeze?** _____

14. Taste the difference between Coke and Pepsi? ○ Absolutely ○ Not really

15. Fave soap scent? _____

16. Last thing you borrowed? _____

17. **Like Scrabble?** ○ **Yes** ○ **No**

18. How 'bout Monopoly? ○ Yes ○ No

19. If u could live 1 day of ur life over, which would u choose? _____

20. *COOLEST CAR YOU'VE BEEN IN?* _____

1. LAST NAME? _____

2. Ever swallowed a non-food item? ○ No ○ Yes, _____.

3. ○ **Speakers** ○ **Headphones** ○ **Ear buds?**

4. Last song you sang out loud? _____

5. Would u mind having wings if it meant u could fly? ○ No ○ Yes

6. What do you put ketchup on? _____

7. HOW 'BOUT MUSTARD? _____

8. Prefer to ○ take ○ be in a photograph?

9. Fave carnival game? _____

10. Tend to blame ○ yourself ○ others ○ a little of both?

11. Best part of a sandwich? _____

12. What's your current mood? _____

13. Fave four-legged creature? _____ Y? _____

14. ○ Fresh fruit ○ Fruit-flavored candy?

15. Last fight I had was about _____

16. Sneakiest place you've ever hidden? _____

17. **Would you like to be cloned?** ○ **Oh yeah** ○ **No way**

18. Fave kind of cheese? _____

19. What does your mouse pad look like? _____

20. ○ **Daredevil** ○ **Scaredy pants?**

WOULD U RATHER

Name

have a spy ○ camera ○ listening device?

be ○ respected for doing the right thing ○ liked for being fun?

○ work really hard and make millions ○ win millions in a contest?

○ sleep in a hammock every night ○ sit in a wooden chair every day?

hang out ○ 1 time with a really cool celebrity ○ for a month with a guy you like?

always have ○ a stain on your shirt ○ something stuck in your front teeth?

have a lifetime of ○ bad hair ○ "I don't like any of my clothes!" days?

be a ○ cat with a litter box ○ dog that has to be taken out?

○ have a cold for 6 months ○ be cold for 6 months?

have the ability to ○ breathe underwater ○ go without sleep?

○ make new friends each year ○ keep your same friends you have now forever?

have ○ 3 eyes ○ 4 arms?

live without ○ salt ○ sugar?

have to wear ○ jeans to work out ○ a formal gown to the movie theater?

always have to wear cowboy ○ boots ○ hat?

Write down another word, sentence or really short story.

Name

POPCORN _____

stars _____

winter _____

texting _____

pirate _____

ELEVATOR _____

castle _____

BOYS _____

furry _____

pebbles _____

red

1. Name you wish you had? _____

2. **Ever tried Red Hot candies?** ◯ No ◯ Yes

3. ◯ **Red** ◯ **Pink roses?**

4. **Look good in red?** ◯ **Not really** ◯ **Some shades** ◯ Yes

5. **Redhead you know?** _____

6. ◯ **Apples** ◯ **Cherries** ◯ **Strawberries?**

7. ◯ **Red lipstick** ◯ **Pink lip gloss** ◯ **Neither?**

8. ◯ **Red** ◯ **Black** ◯ **Refried beans and rice?**

9. **Which movie star rocks the red carpet?** _____

10. ◯ **Cherry Coke** ◯ **Pepsi Wild Cherry?**

rouge
rojo
rosso

11. Which is cooler ... red ◯ dress ◯ shoes ◯ bag?

12. Something red you would not part with? _____

13. Fave character in ruby red slippers movie? _____

14. ◯ Red velvet ◯ Chocolate ◯ Vanilla cake?

15. Valentine's Day is ◯ so overrated ◯ OK, I guess ◯ so sweet.

16. How'd u get your last bad sunburn? _____

17. ◯ Red ◯ Black raspberries?

18. Turn red when you are really mad? ◯ YES! ◯ No

19. How 'bout when you're embarrassed? ◯ Oh yeah ◯ No

20. ◯ Tomato ◯ Cream sauce on pasta?

Ever seen a
shooting star?

1. NICKNAME? _____

2. ○ Sunflower seeds   ○ Peanuts   ○ Granola?

3. Height? ☐ ☐

4. Shoe size? ☐

5. How long have you lived in the house you're in? _____

6. ○ Confetti   ○ Silly string?

7. What do you say when someone sneezes? _____

8. Kind of cell phone u have or want? _____

9. Know what ur name means?   ○ No   ○ Yes, _____ .

10. Fave love song? _____

11. ○ Cheetos   ○ Doritos   ○ Fritos   ○ Tostitos   ○ None of them?

12. Question u would ask the President? _____

13. Comforter pattern & color? _____

14. Trait ur parents love about u? _____

15. Trait of yours that bugs ur parents? _____

16. ○ Rock wall   ○ Mountain climbing?

17. Something u always take with u when u leave the house? _____

18. What makes you fall asleep? _____

19. Oldest thing in your wardrobe? _____ from _____

20. Seen a shooting star? ○ Yes ○ No   Meteor shower? ○ Yes ○ No

I wished I could be a superstar!

1. First name without vowels? _____

2. 3-D movies ○ are really cool ○ make me dizzy.

3. Any exciting news to share? ○ Nope ○ Yep, _____.

4. Fave fair food? ○ Funnel cakes ○ Fried candy bar ○ Sausages ○ Shaved ice

5. I cheer myself up by _____

6. Graffiti is ○ a really cool art form ○ tacky ○ illegal!

7. Shove things under ur bed so ur room looks clean? ○ Oh yeah ○ Uh no

8. Unsolved mystery in ur life? ○ No ○ Yes, _____.

9. ○ Sit-down dinner ○ Eat on the run?

10. COOKIE(S) ○ aND MiLK ○ aND CREaM iCE CREaM ○ DOUGH?

11. Idea for a new reality show? ○ No ○ Yes, _____.

12. Meet anyone new this week? ○ No ○ Yes, _____.

13. Caught a snowflake on your tongue? ○ Yes ○ No

14. States you've lived in? _____

15. Chicken tenders & ○ honey mustard ○ barbeque ○ other _____?

16. Spell well? ○ Yes ○ I'm average ○ No

17. if U were invited to a costume ball, who would U go as? _____

18. ○ Green ○ Black olives ○ Neither, gross!

19. Sat on a rooftop? ○ Yes ○ No

20. FAVE THING TO SLURP THRU A STRAW? _____

Would you really want to be a queen?

1. First name (spelled backwards)? [   ]

2. Playing with a ○ kitten ○ puppy ○ guinea pig is the most fun.

3. WOULD YOU REALLY WANT TO BE A QUEEN? ○ ABSOLUTELY! ○ NO WAY!

4. Most expensive thing you've broken? _____

5. Nails on a chalkboard? ○ AHHH! ○ Doesn't bother me.

6. ○ Love(d) ○ Hate(d) dodgeball?

7. If u could teleport somewhere for 1 day, where would you go? _____

8. Wear/Wore braces? ○ Yes ○ No

9. Like to go barefoot ○ whenever I can ○ sometimes ○ never!

10. Most important thing about you? _____

11. EVER STEPPED ON A NAIL? ○ YES ○ NEVER

12. Look good in hats? ○ No ○ Yes ○ Eh, maybe a few.

13. Last game you won? _____

14. Last game you lost? _____

15. Double dipping is ○ so gross ○ not THAT big of a deal.

16. Ever had food poisoning? ○ Yes, from _____. ○ No

17. Something you've never tried? _____

18. Make any interesting sounds? __ No __Yes, I _____.

19. Popular song you love to hate? _____

20. Ever been hit by a ball? ○ No ○ Yes, I _____.

Absolutely!

Power

1. What do most people call you? _____

2. Wear watch on your ○ **right** ○ **left wrist?**

3. Can you go to bed hungry? ○ Yes ○ No, gotta have something.

4. Last craft you did? _____

5. Ever been in trouble for talking too much? ○ Yep ○ Nah

6. Ever been labeled "shy"? ○ Not hardly ○ A few times ○ Always!

7. Participated in a staring contest? ○ No ○ Yes. Did you win? ○ Yes ○ No

8. Fave kind of socks? _____

9. Arm wrestled? ○ **Yes** ○ **No**

10. Thumb wrestled? ○ Yes ○ No

11. "For real" wrestled? ○ No way ○ Uh, yeah

12. Best thing about the last day of school? _____

13. Worst thing about the last day of school? _____

14. Know a lot of useless trivia? ○ **Yes** ○ **No, not really.**

15. Which color is scarier? ○ Red ○ Black

16. ○ Sweet ○ Sour pickles?

17. BEST FRO-YO IN TOWN? _____

18. Gone backstage at a concert? ○ No ○ Yes, I met _____.

19. ○ Corn on the cob ○ Loose corn niblets?

20. Fave Wii game? _____

BLUE

1. Name

2. What makes you blue?

3. Look good in blue? ● Yes ● No

4. Two blue things in your bedroom?

5. Someone you know with blue eyes?

6. Blueberry ● pancakes ● pie ● smoothie ● muffin?

7. ● Bluebirds ● Blue flowers?

8. ● Baby ● Navy ● Aqua blue?

9. Favorite blue jeans brand?

10. ● Fly the blue sky ● Sail the blue seas?

BLUE

11. Seen the ocean? ◯ No ◯ Yes, I've been to _____.

12. ◯ *Little Mermaid* ◯ *Finding Nemo*?

13. ◯ Submarine ◯ Submarine sandwich?

14. ◯ Ocean bottom ◯ Outer space?

15. I would love to take a cruise to _____.

16. Think SpongeBob will ever get his license? ◯ Yeah ◯ Nah

17. ◯ Crab legs ◯ Crabcake ◯ Krabby patties?

18. Owned a fish besides a goldfish? ◯ No ◯ Yes, a _____.

19. Like calamari? ◯ Yum! ◯ Yuck! ◯ Whatamari?

20. Fave water activity?

1. Middle name? _____

2. IF U COULD GO BACK 24 HOURS, WHAT WOULD U CHANGE? _____

3. Buffets are ○ so much fun ○ germy and gross.

4. Last song you danced to? _____

5. MOVIE THEATER PREVIEWS ARE ○ANNOYING AND LONG ○EXCITING.

6. Coolest old person u know? _____

7. Had anything stolen? ○ No ○ Yes, my _____

8. Most difficult thing you've done? _____

9. Air ○ guitar ○ drums?

10. If u could change ur entire name to one letter, which would u choose?

11. Tallest person you know? _____

12. Ever fainted? ○ No ○ Yes, I _____

13. Own a tiara? ○ No ○ Of course

14. ○ Chili ○ Veggie chili ○ Neither?

15. Old song you really like? _____

16. SHOOK OR KICKED A VENDING MACHINE? ○YES ○NO, IT'S DANGEROUS!

17. Something you love about where u live? _____

18. Something you can't stand about it? _____

19. Care what people think of u? ○ Yeah ○ Depends who it is ○ Nah

20. ○ Karate chopping Styrofoam ○ Popping bubble wrap is more fun!

1. Name? _____

2. Other names for you ur parents considered? _____

3. What r u doing? _____

4. What were u doing this time last year? _____

5. 2nd toe longer than your big toe? ○ Yes ○ No

6. ○ **Wal-Mart** ○ **Target** ○ **Other** _____?

7. I was a ○ good ○ mean ○ hyper ○ weird little kid.

8. name of your very first teacher? _____

9. Did your first teacher like you? ○ Yes ○ No ○ I don't remember

10. Pick change up off the ground? ○ Yes ○ No

11. Sleep with your bedroom door ○ **open** ○ **closed?**

12. ○ Love thunderstorms ○ Lightning freaks me out!

13. ○ I don't want to get married. ○ I would like to be married by age _____.

14. Crying in front of people ○ doesn't bother ○ embarrasses me.

15. Fave symbol, logo, or icon? _____

16. Get motion sickness? ○ Yes ○ No

17. ○ **Lemonade** ○ **Pink lemonade?**

18. ○ M&M's ○ Skittles?

19. Is your family "huggy"? ○ Yep! ○ Not really

20. FASTEST SPEED YOU'VE GONE AT IN A CAR? [____]

two...

1. names you go by? _____

2. people who know you best? _____

3. sweets that go great together? _____

4. things you avoid? _____

5. objects in your backpack or bag? _____

6. things you've climbed? _____

7. places you've jumped from? _____

8. people or things that make u LOL? _____

9. things you've lost? _____

10. things that give u the creeps? _____

11. reasons that make u run fast? _____

12. things you wish existed? _____

13. foods you'd like to eat every day? _____

14. jobs you'd never do? _____

15. activities u do fast? _____

16. activities that take u forever? _____

17. reasons u stay awake @ night? _____

18. sticky things you love? _____

19. things u don't like to do in public? _____

20. things u don't like to do alone? _____

whatdoyouthinkof

when you see or hear these words...

Write down another word, sentence, or really short story.

Name _____

noodles _____

bumblebees _____

HAUNTED HOUSE _____

flip-flops _____

paws _____

fist bump _____

yellow _____

fairy _____

fortune cookies _____

rock band _____

Follow me to your locker
at coke-or-pepsi.com!

I have a doppelganger
my friends say she looks just like me
should I try to find her?

1. **Your last name (in pig Latin)?** _____

2. Have a doppelganger in town (person who looks like you)? ○ Yes ○ No

3. Worst thing you've ever found in your food? _____ in _____.

4. Most annoying fashion trend? _____

5. How do you feel about purple? _____

6. **Are you a pouter?** ○ Oh yeah   ○ Sometimes   ○ Nah

7. What makes you tense? _____

8. Coolest thing about your family? _____

9. Weirdest thing about your family? _____

10. **Snort when you laugh?** ○ Yes ○ Sometimes ○ No

11. Do you make up songs? ○ No ○ Yes R they any good? ○ Yes ○ No

12. Yummiest thing in your fridge right now? _____

13. Grossest thing in your fridge right now? _____

14. ○ **Talking** ○ **Texting on phone?**

15. What would be your superhero name? _____

16. Fave famous athlete? _____

17. How many monogrammed items do you own? _____

18. Best street food? ○ Hot dogs ○ Candied nuts ○ Crepes ○ Pretzels

19. **What could you write a book about?** _____

20. Most interesting person you've ever met? _____

I might be a
little scared...

1. YOUR INITIALS? ●●●

2. ○ Popsicle   ○ Creamsicle   ○ Fudgsicle?

3. How do you spend your allowance? I _____. ○ Don't get one.

4. It would be really cool if _____ were blue instead of _____.

5. Share a bedroom? ○ No   ○ Yes, with _____.

6. 𝕸𝖔𝖘𝖙 𝖕𝖊𝖔𝖕𝖑𝖊 𝖙𝖍𝖎𝖓𝖐 𝕵'𝖒 _____ 𝖇𝖚𝖙 𝕵'𝖒 _____.

7. Best burger in town? _____

8. Ever placed in a science fair?   ○ Yes   ○ No

9. ONE THING YOU THINK IS STUPID? _____

10. If you were a salad dressing, what kind would you be? _____

11. Would you rather eat   ○ in   ○ out?

12. I wish they would create a pill that cured _____ .

13. Ever limbo? ○ No ○ Yes.   Any good? ○ I think so ○ Not really sure

14. **How do you feel about meatloaf?** _____

15. What about fruitcake? _____

16. Good hula hooper? ○ Awesome   ○ So-so   ○ I stink at it!

17. If you could be any age for 1 year, what age would you pick? _____

18. ROOM COLOR THAT BUGS YOU? _____

19. Spend more time in front of a ○ computer ○ TV screen?

20. Fave thing in the world to do? _____

Name . . . .

1. First name with letters mixed up . . . .

2. ◯ Lime ◯ Lemon ◯ Lemon-lime?

3. Ever had a treehouse ? ◯ Yes ◯ No

4. Do u wear green? ◯ No ◯ Yes. Look good in it? ◯ Yes ◯ Dunno

5. Fave green veggie? . . . .

6. ◯ Chartreuse ◯ Grass green ◯ Forest green?

7. Talked with a parrot? ◯ No ◯ Yes. What did it say? . . . .

8. Ever golfed? ◯ No ◯ Just goofy golf ◯ Yes

9. Ever found a four-leaf clover? ◯ Yes ◯ No

10. Most green ($) you've had in your pocket? . . . .

11. Would you try green eggs and ham? ◯ Sure ◯ No way!

12. ◯ Spearmint ◯ Peppermint?

13. Believe in little green men? ◯ Yes! ◯ No, aliens don't exist.

14. Someone you know with green eyes? . . . .

15. Have any Irish in you? ◯ No ◯ Don't know ◯ Yes, ...

16. Like the movie with the Emerald City? ◯ Yes ◯ No, witch is scary!

17. Something that made you green with envy? . . . .

18. ◯ Green ◯ Red apples?

19. Write down the first green thing you see. . . . .

20. What 3 wishes would u ask of a leprechaun? . . . .

UNLIMITED TRAVEL

GET AIR

Would you mind having wings if it meant you could fly?

1. First name upside down? _____

2. Chew on the ends of pencils or pens? ○ Yes ○ No

3. Something you've done that ur friends haven't? _____

4. **What sound makes u laugh?** _____

5. Like hot sauce? ○ Luv it! ○ No

6. Last subject you Googled? _____

7. Something u want to know about the future? _____

8. Do/Did u have Barbie dolls? ○ No ○ Yes. Which kind? _____

9. What's on ur nightstand or next to ur bed? _____

10. **Something you quit?** _____

11. Have a fave Disney princess? ○ No ○ Yes, _____.

12. Want to go to college? ○ No ○ Yes. Where? _____

13. **What makes you sneeze?** _____

14. Taste the difference between Coke and Pepsi? ○ Absolutely ○ Not really

15. Fave soap scent? _____

16. Last thing you borrowed? _____

17. **Like Scrabble?** ○ Yes ○ No

18. How 'bout Monopoly? ○ Yes ○ No

19. If u could live 1 day of ur life over, which would u choose? _____

20. *COOLEST CAR YOU'VE BEEN IN?* _____

1. LAST NAME? _____

2. Ever swallowed a non-food item? ○ No ○ Yes, _____.

3. ○ **Speakers** ○ **Headphones** ○ **Ear buds?**

4. Last song you sang out loud? _____

5. Would u mind having wings if it meant u could fly? ○ No ○ Yes

6. What do you put ketchup on? _____

7. HOW 'bOUT MUSTaRD? _____

8. Prefer to ○ take ○ be in a photograph?

9. Fave carnival game? _____

10. Tend to blame ○ yourself ○ others ○ a little of both?

11. Best part of a sandwich? _____

12. What's your current mood? _____

13. Fave four-legged creature? _____ Y? _____

14. ○ Fresh fruit ○ Fruit–flavored candy?

15. Last fight I had was about _____

16. Sneakiest place you've ever hidden? _____

17. Would you like to be cloned? ○ **Oh yeah** ○ **No way**

18. Fave kind of cheese? _____

19. What does your mouse pad look like? _____

20. ○ **Daredevil** ○ **Scaredy pants?**

WOULD U RATHER...

Name

have a spy ◯ camera ◯ listening device?

be ◯ respected for doing the right thing ◯ liked for being fun?

◯ work really hard and make millions ◯ win millions in a contest?

◯ sleep in a hammock every night ◯ sit in a wooden chair every day?

hang out ◯ 1 time with a really cool celebrity ◯ for a month with a guy you like?

always have ◯ a stain on your shirt ◯ something stuck in your front teeth?

have a lifetime of ◯ bad hair ◯ "I don't like any of my clothes!" days?

be a ◯ cat with a litter box ◯ dog that has to be taken out?

◯ have a cold for 6 months ◯ be cold for 6 months?

have the ability to ◯ breathe underwater ◯ go without sleep?

◯ make new friends each year ◯ keep your same friends you have now forever?

have ◯ 3 eyes ◯ 4 arms?

live without ◯ salt ◯ sugar?

have to wear ◯ jeans to work out ◯ a formal gown to the movie theater?

always have to wear cowboy ◯ boots ◯ hat?

whatdoyouthinkof

when you see or hear these words ...

Write down another word, sentence or really short story.

Name ______________________

POPCORN ______________________

stars ______________________

winter ______________________

texting ______________________

pirate ______________________

ELEVATOR ______________________

castle ______________________

BOYS ______________________

furry ______________________

pebbles ______________________

red

1. Name you wish you had? _____

2. **Ever tried Red Hot candies?** ◯ **No** ◯ **Yes**

3. ◯ **Red** ◯ **Pink roses?**

4. **Look good in red?** ◯ **Not really** ◯ **Some shades** ◯ **Yes**

5. **Redhead you know?** _____

6. ◯ **Apples** ◯ **Cherries** ◯ **Strawberries?**

7. ◯ **Red lipstick** ◯ **Pink lip gloss** ◯ **Neither?**

8. ◯ **Red** ◯ **Black** ◯ **Refried beans and rice?**

9. **Which movie star rocks the red carpet?** _____

10. ◯ **Cherry Coke** ◯ **Pepsi Wild Cherry?**

rouge rojo rosso

11. Which is cooler ... red ◯ dress ◯ shoes ◯ bag?

12. Something red you would not part with? _____

13. Fave character in ruby red slippers movie? _____

14. ◯ Red velvet ◯ Chocolate ◯ Vanilla cake?

15. Valentine's Day is ◯ so overrated ◯ OK, I guess ◯ so sweet.

16. How'd u get your last bad sunburn? _____

17. ◯ Red ◯ Black raspberries?

18. Turn red when you are really mad? ◯ YES! ◯ No

19. How 'bout when you're embarrassed? ◯ Oh yeah ◯ No

20. ◯ Tomato ◯ Cream sauce on pasta?

Ever seen a
shooting star?

1. NICKNAME? _____

2. ◯ Sunflower seeds   ◯ Peanuts   ◯ Granola?

3. Height? ☐ ☐

4. Shoe size? ☐

5. How long have you lived in the house you're in? _____

6. ◯ Confetti   ◯ Silly string?

7. What do you say when someone sneezes? _____

8. Kind of cell phone u have or want? _____

9. Know what ur name means?   ◯ No   ◯ Yes, _____ .

10. Fave love song? _____

11. ◯ Cheetos   ◯ Doritos   ◯ Fritos   ◯ Tostitos   ◯ None of them?

12. Question u would ask the President? _____

13. Comforter pattern & color? _____

14. Trait ur parents love about u? _____

15. Trait of yours that bugs ur parents? _____

16. ◯ **Rock wall**   ◯ **Mountain climbing?**

17. Something u always take with u when u leave the house? _____

18. What makes you fall asleep? _____

19. Oldest thing in your wardrobe? _____ from _____

20. Seen a shooting star? ◯ Yes ◯ No   Meteor shower? ◯ Yes ◯ No

I wished I could be a *superstar!*

1. First name without vowels? _____

2. 3-D movies ○ are really cool ○ make me dizzy.

3. Any exciting news to share? ○ Nope ○ Yep, _____.

4. Fave fair food? ○ Funnel cakes ○ Fried candy bar ○ Sausages ○ Shaved ice

5. I cheer myself up by _____

6. Graffiti is ○ a really cool art form ○ tacky ○ illegal!

7. Shove things under ur bed so ur room looks clean? ○ Oh yeah ○ Uh no

8. Unsolved mystery in ur life? ○ No ○ Yes, _____.

9. ○ Sit-down dinner ○ Eat on the run?

10. COOKiE(S) ○ aND MiLK ○ aND CREaM iCE CREaM ○ DOUGH?

11. Idea for a new reality show? ○ No ○ Yes, _____.

12. Meet anyone new this week? ○ No ○ Yes, _____.

13. Caught a snowflake on your tongue? ○ Yes ○ No

14. States you've lived in? _____

15. Chicken tenders & ○ honey mustard ○ barbeque ○ other _____?

16. Spell well? ○ Yes ○ I'm average ○ No

17. if U Were iNViTED TO a COSTUME ball, WHO WOULD U gO aS? _____

18. ○ Green ○ Black olives ○ Neither, gross!

19. Sat on a rooftop? ○ Yes ○ No

20. FAVE THING TO SLURP THRU A STRAW? _____

Would you really want to be a queen?

1. First name (spelled backwards)? [_____]

2. Playing with a ○ kitten ○ puppy ○ guinea pig is the most fun.

3. WOULD YOU REALLY WANT TO BE A QUEEN? ○ ABSOLUTELY! ○ NO WAY!

4. Most expensive thing you've broken? _____

5. Nails on a chalkboard? ○ AHHH! ○ Doesn't bother me.

6. ○ Love(d) ○ Hate(d) dodgeball?

7. If u could teleport somewhere for 1 day, where would you go? _____

8. Wear/Wore braces? ○ Yes ○ No

9. Like to go barefoot ○ whenever I can ○ sometimes ○ never!

10. Most important thing about you? _____

11. EVER STEPPED ON A NAIL? ○ YES ○ NEVER

12. Look good in hats? ○ No ○ Yes ○ Eh, maybe a few.

13. Last game you won? _____

14. Last game you lost? _____

15. Double dipping is ○ so gross ○ not THAT big of a deal.

16. Ever had food poisoning? ○ Yes, from _____. ○ No

17. Something you've never tried? _____

18. Make any interesting sounds? __ No __ Yes, I _____.

19. Popular song you love to hate? _____

20. Ever been hit by a ball? ○ No ○ Yes, I _____.

Absolutely!

Power

1. What do most people call you? _____

2. Wear watch on your ○ right ○ left wrist?

3. Can you go to bed hungry? ○ Yes ○ No, gotta have something.

4. Last craft you did? _____

5. Ever been in trouble for talking too much? ○ Yep ○ Nah

6. Ever been labeled "shy"? ○ Not hardly ○ A few times ○ Always!

7. Participated in a staring contest? ○ No ○ Yes. Did you win? ○ Yes ○ No

8. Fave kind of socks? _____

9. Arm wrestled? ○ Yes ○ No

10. Thumb wrestled? ○ Yes ○ No

11. "For real" wrestled? ○ No way ○ Uh, yeah

12. Best thing about the last day of school? _____

13. Worst thing about the last day of school? _____

14. Know a lot of useless trivia? ○ Yes ○ No, not really.

15. Which color is scarier? ○ Red ○ Black

16. ○ Sweet ○ Sour pickles?

17. BEST FRO-YO IN TOWN? _____

18. Gone backstage at a concert? ○ No ○ Yes, I met _____.

19. ○ Corn on the cob ○ Loose corn niblets?

20. Fave Wii game? _____

BLUE

1. Name

2. What makes you blue?

3. Look good in blue? ● Yes ● No

4. Two blue things in your bedroom?

5. Someone you know with blue eyes?

6. Blueberry ● pancakes ● pie ● smoothie ● muffin?

7. ● Bluebirds ● Blue flowers?

8. ● Baby ● Navy ● Aqua blue?

9. Favorite blue jeans brand?

10. ● Fly the blue sky ● Sail the blue seas?

BLUE

11. Seen the ocean? ○ No ○ Yes, I've been to _____.

12. ○ *Little Mermaid* ○ *Finding Nemo?*

13. ○ Submarine ○ Submarine sandwich?

14. ○ Ocean bottom ○ Outer space?

15. I would love to take a cruise to _____.

16. Think SpongeBob will ever get his license? ○ Yeah ○ Nah

17. ○ Crab legs ○ Crabcake ○ Krabby patties?

18. Owned a fish besides a goldfish? ○ No ○ Yes, a _____.

19. Like calamari? ○ Yum! ○ Yuck! ○ Whatamari?

20. Fave water activity?

1. Middle name? _____

2. IF U COULD GO BACK 24 HOURS, WHAT WOULD U CHANGE? _____

3. Buffets are ○ so much fun ○ germy and gross.

4. Last song you danced to? _____

5. MOVIE THEATER PREVIEWS ARE ○ANNOYING AND LONG ○EXCITING.

6. Coolest old person u know? _____

7. Had anything stolen? ○ No ○ Yes, my _____

8. Most difficult thing you've done? _____

9. Air ○ guitar ○ drums?

10. If u could change ur entire name to one letter, which would u choose? ☐

11. Tallest person you know? _____

12. Ever fainted? ○ No ○ Yes, I _____

13. Own a tiara? ○ No ○ Of course

14. ○ Chili ○ Veggie chili ○ Neither?

15. Old song you really like? _____

16. SHOOK OR KICKED A VENDING MACHINE? ○YES ○NO, IT'S DANGEROUS!

17. Something you love about where u live? _____

18. Something you can't stand about it? _____

19. Care what people think of u? ○ Yeah ○ Depends who it is ○ Nah

20. ○ Karate chopping Styrofoam ○ Popping bubble wrap is more fun!

1. Name? _____

2. Other names for you ur parents considered? _____

3. What r u doing? _____

4. What were u doing this time last year? _____

5. 2nd toe longer than your big toe? ○ Yes ○ No

6. ○ Wal-Mart ○ Target ○ Other _____?

7. I was a ○ good ○ mean ○ hyper ○ weird little kid.

8. name of your very first teacher? _____

9. Did your first teacher like you? ○ Yes ○ No ○ I don't remember

10. Pick change up off the ground? ○ Yes ○ No

11. Sleep with your bedroom door ○ open ○ closed?

12. ○ Love thunderstorms ○ Lightning freaks me out!

13. ○ I don't want to get married. ○ I would like to be married by age _____.

14. Crying in front of people ○ doesn't bother ○ embarrasses me.

15. Fave symbol, logo, or icon? _____

16. Get motion sickness? ○ Yes ○ No

17. ○ Lemonade ○ Pink lemonade?

18. ○ M&M's ○ Skittles?

19. Is your family "huggy"? ○ Yep! ○ Not really

20. FASTEST SPEED YOU'VE GONE AT IN A CAR? [   ]

two...

1. names you go by? _____

2. people who know you best? _____

3. sweets that go great together? _____

4. things you avoid? _____

5. objects in your backpack or bag? _____

6. things you've climbed? _____

7. places you've jumped from? _____

8. people or things that make u LOL? _____

9. things you've lost? _____

10. things that give u the creeps? _____

11. reasons that make u run fast? _____

12. things you wish existed? _____

13. foods you'd like to eat every day? _____

14. jobs you'd never do? _____

15. activities u do fast? _____

16. activities that take u forever? _____

17. reasons u stay awake @ night? _____

18. sticky things you love? _____

19. things u don't like to do in public? _____

20. things u don't like to do alone? _____

whatdoyouthinkof

when you see or hear these words ...

Write down another word, sentence, or really short story.

Name _____

noodles _____

bumblebees _____

HAUNTED HOUSE _____

flip-flops _____

paws _____

fist bump _____

yellow _____

fairy _____

fortune cookies _____

rock band _____

Follow me to your locker
at coke-or-pepsi.com!

Find more questions and free stuff in your personal locker at
coke-or-pepsi.com/locker. Your secret combination is 7-25-40.

I have a doppelganger
my friends say she looks just like me
should I try to find her?

1. Your last name (in pig Latin)? _____

2. Have a doppelganger in town (person who looks like you)? ○ Yes ○ No

3. Worst thing you've ever found in your food? _____ in _____.

4. Most annoying fashion trend? _____

5. How do you feel about purple? _____

6. Are you a pouter? ○ Oh yeah ○ Sometimes ○ Nah

7. What makes you tense? _____

8. Coolest thing about your family? _____

9. Weirdest thing about your family? _____

10. Snort when you laugh? ○ Yes ○ Sometimes ○ No

11. Do you make up songs? ○ No ○ Yes R they any good? ○ Yes ○ No

12. Yummiest thing in your fridge right now? _____

13. Grossest thing in your fridge right now? _____

14. ○ Talking ○ Texting on phone?

15. What would be your superhero name? _____

16. Fave famous athlete? _____

17. How many monogrammed items do you own? _____

18. Best street food? ○ Hot dogs ○ Candied nuts ○ Crepes ○ Pretzels

19. What could you write a book about? _____

20. Most interesting person you've ever met? _____

I might be a little scared...

1. YOUR INITIALS?

2. ○ Popsicle ○ Creamsicle ○ Fudgsicle?

3. How do you spend your allowance? I _____. ○ Don't get one.

4. It would be really cool if _____ were blue instead of _____.

5. Share a bedroom? ○ No ○ Yes, with _____.

6. Most people think I'm _____ but I'm _____.

7. Best burger in town? _____

8. Ever placed in a science fair? ○ Yes ○ No

9. ONE THING YOU THINK IS STUPID? _____

10. If you were a salad dressing, what kind would you be? _____

11. Would you rather eat ○ in ○ out?

12. I wish they would create a pill that cured _____ .

13. Ever limbo? ○ No ○ Yes. Any good? ○ I think so ○ Not really sure

14. **How do you feel about meatloaf?** _____

15. What about fruitcake? _____

16. Good hula hooper? ○ Awesome ○ So-so ○ I stink at it!

17. If you could be any age for 1 year, what age would you pick? _____

18. ROOM COLOR THAT BUGS YOU? _____

19. Spend more time in front of a ○ computer ○ TV screen?

20. Fave thing in the world to do? _____

Name . . . .

1. First name with letters mixed up . . . .

2. ○ Lime ○ Lemon ○ Lemon-lime?

3. Ever had a treehouse ? ○ Yes ○ No

4. Do u wear green? ○ No ○ Yes. Look good in it? ○ Yes ○ Dunno

5. Fave green veggie? . . . .

6. ○ Chartreuse ○ Grass green ○ Forest green?

7. Talked with a parrot? ○ No ○ Yes. What did it say? . . . .

8. Ever golfed? ○ No ○ Just goofy golf ○ Yes

9. Ever found a four-leaf clover? ○ Yes ○ No

10. Most green ($) you've had in your pocket? . . . .

11. Would you try green eggs and ham? ◯ Sure ◯ No way!

12. ◯ Spearmint ◯ Peppermint?

13. Believe in little green men? ◯ Yes! ◯ No, aliens don't exist.

14. Someone you know with green eyes? . . . .

15. Have any Irish in you? ◯ No ◯ Don't know ◯ Yes, ...

16. Like the movie with the Emerald City? ◯ Yes ◯ No, witch is scary!

17. Something that made you green with envy? . . . .

18. ◯ Green ◯ Red apples?

19. Write down the first green thing you see. . . . .

20. What 3 wishes would u ask of a leprechaun? . . . .

GET
AIR

UNLIMITED TRAVEL

*Would you mind having wings
if it meant you could fly?*

1. **First name upside down?** _____

2. Chew on the ends of pencils or pens? ◯ Yes ◯ No

3. Something you've done that ur friends haven't? _____

4. **What sound makes u laugh?** _____

5. Like hot sauce? ◯ Luv it! ◯ No

6. Last subject you Googled? _____

7. Something u want to know about the future? _____

8. Do/Did u have Barbie dolls? ◯ No ◯ Yes. Which kind? _____

9. What's on ur nightstand or next to ur bed? _____

10. **Something you quit?** _____

11. Have a fave Disney princess? ◯ No ◯ Yes, _____.

12. Want to go to college? ◯ No ◯ Yes. Where? _____

13. **What makes you sneeze?** _____

14. Taste the difference between Coke and Pepsi? ◯ Absolutely ◯ Not really

15. Fave soap scent? _____

16. Last thing you borrowed? _____

17. **Like Scrabble?** ◯ Yes ◯ No

18. How 'bout Monopoly? ◯ Yes ◯ No

19. If u could live 1 day of ur life over, which would u choose? _____

20. *COOLEST CAR YOU'VE BEEN IN?* _____

I would fly straight to the moon.

1. LAST NAME? _____

2. Ever swallowed a non-food item? ○ No ○ Yes, _____.

3. ○ **Speakers**   ○ **Headphones**   ○ **Ear buds?**

4. Last song you sang out loud? _____

5. Would u mind having wings if it meant u could fly? ○ No   ○ Yes

6. What do you put ketchup on? _____

7. HOW 'bOUT MUSTARD? _____

8. Prefer to ○ take ○ be in a photograph?

9. Fave carnival game? _____

10. Tend to blame ○ yourself ○ others ○ a little of both?

11. Best part of a sandwich? _____

12. What's your current mood? _____

13. Fave four-legged creature? _____ Y? _____

14. ○ Fresh fruit   ○ Fruit-flavored candy?

15. Last fight I had was about _____

16. Sneakiest place you've ever hidden? _____

17. Would you like to be cloned? ○ **Oh yeah** ○ **No way**

18. Fave kind of cheese? _____

19. What does your mouse pad look like? _____

20. ○ **Daredevil** ○ **Scaredy pants?**

WOULD U RATHER...

Name

have a spy ◯ camera ◯ listening device?

be ◯ respected for doing the right thing ◯ liked for being fun?

◯ work really hard and make millions ◯ win millions in a contest?

◯ sleep in a hammock every night ◯ sit in a wooden chair every day?

hang out ◯ 1 time with a really cool celebrity ◯ for a month with a guy you like?

always have ◯ a stain on your shirt ◯ something stuck in your front teeth?

have a lifetime of ◯ bad hair ◯ "I don't like any of my clothes!" days?

be a ◯ cat with a litter box ◯ dog that has to be taken out?

◯ have a cold for 6 months ◯ be cold for 6 months?

have the ability to ◯ breathe underwater ◯ go without sleep?

◯ make new friends each year ◯ keep your same friends you have now forever?

have ◯ 3 eyes ◯ 4 arms?

live without ◯ salt ◯ sugar?

have to wear ◯ jeans to work out ◯ a formal gown to the movie theater?

always have to wear cowboy ◯ boots ◯ hat?

Whatdoyouthinkof
when you see or hear these words ...

Write down another word, sentence or really short story.

Name

POPCORN _____

stars _____

winter _____

texting _____

pirate _____

ELEVATOR _____

castle _____

BOYS _____

furry _____

pebbles _____

red

1. Name you wish you had? _____

2. **Ever tried Red Hot candies?** ◯ **No** ◯ **Yes**

3. ◯ **Red** ◯ **Pink roses?**

4. **Look good in red?** ◯ **Not really** ◯ **Some shades** ◯ **Yes**

5. **Redhead you know?** _____

6. ◯ **Apples** ◯ **Cherries** ◯ **Strawberries?**

7. ◯ **Red lipstick** ◯ **Pink lip gloss** ◯ **Neither?**

8. ◯ **Red** ◯ **Black** ◯ **Refried beans and rice?**

9. **Which movie star rocks the red carpet?** _____

10. ◯ **Cherry Coke** ◯ **Pepsi Wild Cherry?**

rouge
rojo
rosso

11. Which is cooler … red ◯ dress ◯ shoes ◯ bag?

12. Something red you would not part with? _____

13. Fave character in ruby red slippers movie? _____

14. ◯ Red velvet ◯ Chocolate ◯ Vanilla cake?

15. Valentine's Day is ◯ so overrated ◯ OK, I guess ◯ so sweet.

16. How'd u get your last bad sunburn? _____

17. ◯ Red ◯ Black raspberries?

18. Turn red when you are really mad? ◯ YES! ◯ No

19. How 'bout when you're embarrassed? ◯ Oh yeah ◯ No

20. ◯ Tomato ◯ Cream sauce on pasta?

Ever seen a shooting star?

1. NICKNAME? _____

2. ○ Sunflower seeds   ○ Peanuts   ○ Granola?

3. Height? ☐ ☐

4. Shoe size? ☐

5. How long have you lived in the house you're in? _____

6. ○ Confetti   ○ Silly string?

7. What do you say when someone sneezes? _____

8. Kind of cell phone u have or want? _____

9. Know what ur name means? ○ No ○ Yes, _____ .

10. Fave love song? _____

11. ○ Cheetos ○ Doritos   ○ Fritos   ○ Tostitos   ○ None of them?

12. Question u would ask the President? _____

13. Comforter pattern & color? _____

14. Trait ur parents love about u? _____

15. Trait of yours that bugs ur parents? _____

16. ○ Rock wall   ○ Mountain climbing?

17. Something u always take with u when u leave the house? _____

18. What makes you fall asleep? _____

19. Oldest thing in your wardrobe? _____ from _____

20. Seen a shooting star? ○ Yes ○ No   Meteor shower? ○ Yes ○ No

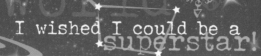

I wished I could be a superstar!

1. First name without vowels? _____

2. 3-D movies ○ are really cool ○ make me dizzy.

3. Any exciting news to share? ○ Nope ○ Yep, _____.

4. Fave fair food? ○ Funnel cakes ○ Fried candy bar ○ Sausages ○ Shaved ice

5. I cheer myself up by _____

6. Graffiti is ○ a really cool art form ○ tacky ○ illegal!

7. Shove things under ur bed so ur room looks clean? ○ Oh yeah ○ Uh no

8. Unsolved mystery in ur life? ○ No ○ Yes, _____.

9. ○ Sit-down dinner ○ Eat on the run?

10. COOKIE(S) ○ aND MiLK ○ aND CREaM iCE CREaM ○ DOUGH?

11. Idea for a new reality show? ○ No ○ Yes, _____.

12. Meet anyone new this week? ○ No ○ Yes, _____.

13. Caught a snowflake on your tongue? ○ Yes ○ No

14. States you've lived in? _____

15. Chicken tenders & ○ honey mustard ○ barbeque ○ other _____?

16. Spell well? ○ Yes ○ I'm average ○ No

17. iF U WERE iNViTED TO a COSTUME baLL, WHO WOULD U GO aS? _____

18. ○ Green ○ Black olives ○ Neither, gross!

19. Sat on a rooftop? ○ Yes ○ No

20. FAVE THING TO SLURP THRU A STRAW? _____

Would you really want to be a queen?

1. First name (spelled backwards)? _____

2. Playing with a ◯ kitten ◯ puppy ◯ guinea pig is the most fun.

3. WOULD YOU REALLY WANT TO BE A QUEEN? ◯ ABSOLUTELY! ◯ NO WAY!

4. Most expensive thing you've broken? _____

5. Nails on a chalkboard? ◯ AHHH! ◯ Doesn't bother me.

6. ◯ Love(d) ◯ Hate(d) dodgeball?

7. If u could teleport somewhere for 1 day, where would you go? _____

8. Wear/Wore braces? ◯ Yes ◯ No

9. Like to go barefoot ◯ whenever I can ◯ sometimes ◯ never!

10. Most important thing about you? _____

11. EVER STEPPED ON A NAIL? ◯ YES ◯ NEVER

12. Look good in hats? ◯ No ◯ Yes ◯ Eh, maybe a few.

13. Last game you won? _____

14. Last game you lost? _____

15. Double dipping is ◯ so gross ◯ not THAT big of a deal.

16. Ever had food poisoning? ◯ Yes, from _____. ◯ No

17. Something you've never tried? _____

18. Make any interesting sounds? __ No __ Yes, I _____.

19. Popular song you love to hate? _____

20. Ever been hit by a ball? ◯ No ◯ Yes, I _____.

Unlimi

Power

1. What do most people call you?

2. Wear watch on your ○ right ○ left wrist?

3. Can you go to bed hungry? ○ Yes ○ No, gotta have something.

4. Last craft you did? _____

5. Ever been in trouble for talking too much? ○ Yep ○ Nah

6. Ever been labeled "shy"? ○ Not hardly ○ A few times ○ Always!

7. Participated in a staring contest? ○ No ○ Yes.   Did you win? ○ Yes ○ No

8. Fave kind of socks? _____

9. Arm wrestled? ○ **Yes** ○ **No**

10. Thumb wrestled? ○ Yes ○ No

11. "For real" wrestled? ○ No way ○ Uh, yeah

12. Best thing about the last day of school? _____

13. Worst thing about the last day of school? _____

14. Know a lot of useless trivia? ○ **Yes** ○ **No, not really.**

15. Which color is scarier? ○ Red ○ Black

16. ○ Sweet ○ Sour pickles?

17. BEST FRO-YO IN TOWN? _____

18. Gone backstage at a concert? ○ No ○ Yes, I met _____.

19. ○ Corn on the cob ○ Loose corn niblets?

20. Fave Wii game?_____

BLUE

1. Name

2. What makes you blue?

3. Look good in blue? ● Yes ● No

4. Two blue things in your bedroom?

5. Someone you know with blue eyes?

6. Blueberry ● pancakes ● pie ● smoothie ● muffin?

7. ● Bluebirds ● Blue flowers?

8. ● Baby ● Navy ● Aqua blue?

9. Favorite blue jeans brand?

10. ● Fly the blue sky ● Sail the blue seas?

BLUE

11. Seen the ocean? ◯ No ◯ Yes, I've been to _____.

12. ◯ *Little Mermaid* ◯ *Finding Nemo?*

13. ◯ Submarine ◯ Submarine sandwich?

14. ◯ Ocean bottom ◯ Outer space?

15. I would love to take a cruise to _____.

16. Think SpongeBob will ever get his license? ◯ Yeah ◯ Nah

17. ◯ Crab legs ◯ Crabcake ◯ Krabby patties?

18. Owned a fish besides a goldfish? ◯ No ◯ Yes, a _____.

19. Like calamari? ◯ Yum! ◯ Yuck! ◯ Whatamari?

20. Fave water activity?

unlimited ♡♡

unlimited possibilities...

1. Middle name? _____

2. IF U COULD GO BACK 24 HOURS, WHAT WOULD U CHANGE? _____

3. Buffets are ○ so much fun ○ germy and gross.

4. Last song you danced to? _____

5. MOVIE THEATER PREVIEWS ARE ○ANNOYING AND LONG ○EXCITING.

6. Coolest old person u know? _____

7. Had anything stolen? ○ No ○ Yes, my _____

8. Most difficult thing you've done? _____

9. Air ○ guitar ○ drums?

10. If u could change ur entire name to one letter, which would u choose? ▢

11. Tallest person you know? _____

12. Ever fainted? ○ No ○ Yes, I _____

13. Own a tiara? ○ No ○ Of course

14. ○ Chili ○ Veggie chili ○ Neither?

15. Old song you really like? _____

16. SHOOK OR KICKED A VENDING MACHINE? ○ YES ○ NO, IT'S DANGEROUS!

17. Something you love about where u live? _____

18. Something you can't stand about it? _____

19. Care what people think of u? ○ Yeah ○ Depends who it is ○ Nah

20. ○ Karate chopping Styrofoam ○ Popping bubble wrap is more fun!

1. Name? _____

2. Other names for you ur parents considered? _____

3. What r u doing? _____

4. What were u doing this time last year? _____

5. 2nd toe longer than your big toe? ○ Yes ○ No

6. ○ **Wal-Mart** ○ **Target** ○ **Other** _____?

7. I was a ○ good ○ mean ○ hyper ○ weird little kid.

8. name of your very first teacher? _____

9. Did your first teacher like you? ○ Yes ○ No ○ I don't remember

10. Pick change up off the ground? ○ Yes ○ No

11. Sleep with your bedroom door ○ **open** ○ **closed?**

12. ○ Love thunderstorms ○ Lightning freaks me out!

13. ○ I don't want to get married. ○ I would like to be married by age _____.

14. Crying in front of people ○ doesn't bother ○ embarrasses me.

15. Fave symbol, logo, or icon? _____

16. Get motion sickness? ○ Yes ○ No

17. ○ **Lemonade** ○ **Pink lemonade?**

18. ○ M&M's ○ Skittles?

19. Is your family "huggy"? ○ Yep! ○ Not really

20. FASTEST SPEED YOU'VE GONE AT IN A CAR? [_____]

two...

1. names you go by? _____

2. people who know you best? _____

3. sweets that go great together? _____

4. things you avoid? _____

5. objects in your backpack or bag? _____

6. things you've climbed? _____

7. places you've jumped from? _____

8. people or things that make u LOL? _____

9. things you've lost? _____

10. things that give u the creeps? _____

11. reasons that make u run fast? _____

12. things you wish existed? _____

13. foods you'd like to eat every day? _____

14. jobs you'd never do? _____

15. activities u do fast? _____

16. activities that take u forever? _____

17. reasons u stay awake @ night? _____

18. sticky things you love? _____

19. things u don't like to do in public? _____

20. things u don't like to do alone? _____

Whatdoyouthinkof
when you see or hear these words...

Write down another word, sentence, or really short story.

Name

noodles _____

bumblebees _____

HAUNTED HOUSE _____

flip-flops _____

paws _____

fist bump _____

yellow _____

fairy _____

fortune cookies _____

rock band _____

Follow me to your locker
at coke-or-pepsi.com!

Find more questions and free stuff in your personal locker at
coke-or-pepsi.com/locker. Your secret combination is 6-25-38.

I have a doppelganger
my friends say she looks just like me
should I try to find her?

1. Your last name (in pig Latin)? _____

2. Have a doppelganger in town (person who looks like you)? ○ Yes ○ No

3. Worst thing you've ever found in your food? _____ in _____.

4. Most annoying fashion trend? _____

5. How do you feel about purple? _____

6. Are you a pouter? ○ Oh yeah   ○ Sometimes   ○ Nah

7. What makes you tense? _____

8. Coolest thing about your family? _____

9. Weirdest thing about your family? _____

10. Snort when you laugh? ○ Yes ○ Sometimes ○ No

11. Do you make up songs? ○ No ○ Yes R they any good? ○ Yes ○ No

12. Yummiest thing in your fridge right now? _____

13. Grossest thing in your fridge right now? _____

14. ○ Talking ○ Texting on phone?

15. What would be your superhero name? _____

16. Fave famous athlete? _____

17. How many monogrammed items do you own? _____

18. Best street food? ○ Hot dogs ○ Candied nuts ○ Crepes ○ Pretzels

19. What could you write a book about? _____

20. Most interesting person you've ever met? _____

I might be a
little scared...

1. YOUR INITIALS? ● ● ●

2. ○ Popsicle   ○ Creamsicle   ○ Fudgsicle?

3. How do you spend your allowance? I _____. ○ Don't get one.

4. It would be really cool if _____ were blue instead of _____.

5. Share a bedroom? ○ No   ○ Yes, with _____.

6. 𝕸𝖔𝖘𝖙 𝖕𝖊𝖔𝖕𝖑𝖊 𝖙𝖍𝖎𝖓𝖐 𝕴'𝖒 _____ 𝖇𝖚𝖙 𝕴'𝖒 _____.

7. Best burger in town? _____

8. Ever placed in a science fair? ○ Yes   ○ No

9. ONE THING YOU THINK IS STUPID? _____

10. If you were a salad dressing, what kind would you be? _____

11. Would you rather eat ○ in ○ out?

12. I wish they would create a pill that cured _____.

13. Ever limbo? ○ No ○ Yes. Any good? ○ I think so ○ Not really sure

14. **How do you feel about meatloaf?** _____

15. What about fruitcake? _____

16. Good hula hooper? ○ Awesome ○ So-so ○ I stink at it!

17. If you could be any age for 1 year, what age would you pick? _____

18. ROOM COLOR THAT BUGS YOU? _____

19. Spend more time in front of a ○ computer ○ TV screen?

20. Fave thing in the world to do? _____

Name . . . .

1. First name with letters mixed up . . . .

2. ◯ Lime ◯ Lemon ◯ Lemon-lime?

3. Ever had a treehouse ? ◯ Yes ◯ No

4. Do u wear green? ◯ No ◯ Yes. Look good in it? ◯ Yes ◯ Dunno

5. Fave green veggie? . . . .

6. ◯ Chartreuse ◯ Grass green ◯ Forest green?

7. Talked with a parrot? ◯ No ◯ Yes. What did it say? . . . .

8. Ever golfed? ◯ No ◯ Just goofy golf ◯ Yes

9. Ever found a four-leaf clover? ◯ Yes ◯ No

10. Most green ($) you've had in your pocket? . . . .

11. Would you try green eggs and ham? ○ Sure ○ No way!

12. ○ Spearmint ○ Peppermint?

13. Believe in little green men? ○ Yes! ○ No, aliens don't exist.

14. Someone you know with green eyes? . . . .

15. Have any Irish in you? ○ No ○ Don't know ○ Yes, ...

16. Like the movie with the Emerald City? ○ Yes ○ No, witch is scary!

17. Something that made you green with envy? . . . .

18. ○ Green ○ Red apples?

19. Write down the first green thing you see. . . . .

20. What 3 wishes would u ask of a leprechaun? . . . .

GET AIR

Would you mind having wings
if it meant you could fly?

1. First name upside down? _____

2. Chew on the ends of pencils or pens? ◯ Yes ◯ No

3. Something you've done that ur friends haven't? _____

4. What sound makes u laugh? _____

5. Like hot sauce? ◯ Luv it! ◯ No

6. Last subject you Googled? _____

7. Something u want to know about the future? _____

8. Do/Did u have Barbie dolls? ◯ No ◯ Yes. Which kind? _____

9. What's on ur nightstand or next to ur bed? _____

10. Something you quit? _____

11. Have a fave Disney princess? ◯ No ◯ Yes, _____.

12. Want to go to college? ◯ No ◯ Yes. Where? _____

13. What makes you sneeze? _____

14. Taste the difference between Coke and Pepsi? ◯ Absolutely ◯ Not really

15. Fave soap scent? _____

16. Last thing you borrowed? _____

17. Like Scrabble? ◯ Yes ◯ No

18. How 'bout Monopoly? ◯ Yes ◯ No

19. If u could live 1 day of ur life over, which would u choose? _____

20. COOLEST CAR YOU'VE BEEN IN? _____

I would fly straight to the moon.

1. LAST NAME? _____

2. Ever swallowed a non-food item? ○ No ○ Yes, _____.

3. ○ **Speakers**   ○ **Headphones**   ○ **Ear buds?**

4. Last song you sang out loud? _____

5. Would u mind having wings if it meant u could fly? ○ No   ○ Yes

6. What do you put ketchup on? _____

7. HOW 'bOUT MUSTARD? _____

8. Prefer to ○ take ○ be in a photograph?

9. Fave carnival game? _____

10. Tend to blame ○ yourself ○ others ○ a little of both?

11. Best part of a sandwich? _____

12. What's your current mood? _____

13. Fave four-legged creature? _____ Y? _____

14. ○ Fresh fruit   ○ Fruit-flavored candy?

15. Last fight I had was about _____

16. Sneakiest place you've ever hidden? _____

17. **Would you like to be cloned?** ○ **Oh yeah** ○ **No way**

18. Fave kind of cheese? _____

19. What does your mouse pad look like? _____

20. ○ **Daredevil** ○ **Scaredy pants?**

WOULD U RATHER...

Name _____

have a spy ○ camera ○ listening device?

be ○ respected for doing the right thing ○ liked for being fun?

○ work really hard and make millions ○ win millions in a contest?

○ sleep in a hammock every night ○ sit in a wooden chair every day?

hang out ○ 1 time with a really cool celebrity ○ for a month with a guy you like?

always have ○ a stain on your shirt ○ something stuck in your front teeth?

have a lifetime of ○ bad hair ○ "I don't like any of my clothes!" days?

be a ○ cat with a litter box ○ dog that has to be taken out?

○ have a cold for 6 months ○ be cold for 6 months?

have the ability to ○ breathe underwater ○ go without sleep?

○ make new friends each year ○ keep your same friends you have now forever?

have ○ 3 eyes ○ 4 arms?

live without ○ salt ○ sugar?

have to wear ○ jeans to work out ○ a formal gown to the movie theater?

always have to wear cowboy ○ boots ○ hat?

whatdoyouthinkof

when you see or hear these words ...

Write down another word, sentence or really short story.

Name

POPCORN _____

stars _____

winter _____

texting _____

pirate _____

ELEVATOR _____

castle _____

BOYS _____

furry _____

pebbles _____

red

1. Name you wish you had? _____

2. Ever tried Red Hot candies? ◯ No ◯ Yes

3. ◯ Red ◯ Pink roses?

4. Look good in red? ◯ Not really ◯ Some shades ◯ Yes

5. Redhead you know? _____

6. ◯ Apples ◯ Cherries ◯ Strawberries?

7. ◯ Red lipstick ◯ Pink lip gloss ◯ Neither?

8. ◯ Red ◯ Black ◯ Refried beans and rice?

9. Which movie star rocks the red carpet? _____

10. ◯ Cherry Coke ◯ Pepsi Wild Cherry?

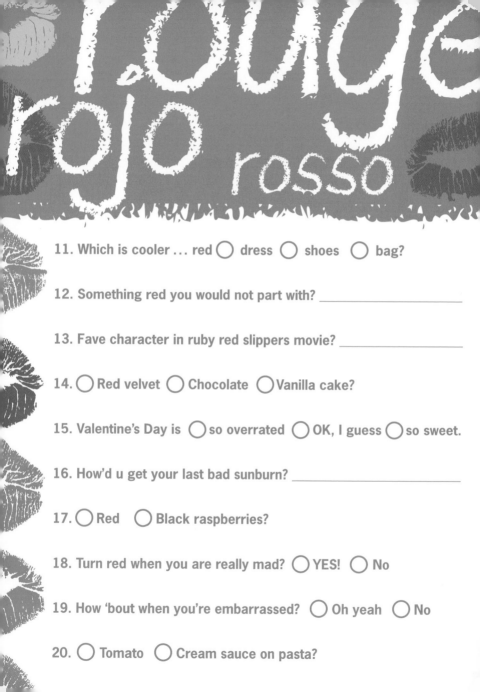

rouge

rojo

rosso

11. Which is cooler ... red ○ dress ○ shoes ○ bag?

12. Something red you would not part with? _____

13. Fave character in ruby red slippers movie? _____

14. ○ Red velvet ○ Chocolate ○ Vanilla cake?

15. Valentine's Day is ○ so overrated ○ OK, I guess ○ so sweet.

16. How'd u get your last bad sunburn? _____

17. ○ Red ○ Black raspberries?

18. Turn red when you are really mad? ○ YES! ○ No

19. How 'bout when you're embarrassed? ○ Oh yeah ○ No

20. ○ Tomato ○ Cream sauce on pasta?

Ever seen a shooting star?

1. NICKNAME? _____

2. ○ Sunflower seeds   ○ Peanuts   ○ Granola?

3. Height? ☐ ☐

4. Shoe size? ☐

5. How long have you lived in the house you're in? _____

6. ○ Confetti   ○ Silly string?

7. What do you say when someone sneezes? _____

8. Kind of cell phone u have or want? _____

9. Know what ur name means? ○ No ○ Yes, _____ .

10. Fave love song? _____

11. ○ Cheetos   ○ Doritos   ○ Fritos   ○ Tostitos   ○ None of them?

12. Question u would ask the President? _____

13. Comforter pattern & color? _____

14. Trait ur parents love about u? _____

15. Trait of yours that bugs ur parents? _____

16. ○ Rock wall   ○ Mountain climbing?

17. Something u always take with u when u leave the house? _____

18. What makes you fall asleep? _____

19. Oldest thing in your wardrobe? _____ from _____

20. Seen a shooting star? ○ Yes ○ No   Meteor shower? ○ Yes ○ No

1. First name without vowels? _____

2. 3-D movies ○ are really cool ○ make me dizzy.

3. Any exciting news to share? ○ Nope ○ Yep, _____.

4. Fave fair food? ○ Funnel cakes ○ Fried candy bar ○ Sausages ○ Shaved ice

5. I cheer myself up by _____

6. Graffiti is ○ a really cool art form ○ tacky ○ illegal!

7. Shove things under ur bed so ur room looks clean? ○ Oh yeah ○ Uh no

8. Unsolved mystery in ur life? ○ No ○ Yes, _____.

9. ○ Sit-down dinner ○ Eat on the run?

10. COOKIE(S) ○ aND MILK ○ aND CREAM ICE CREAM ○ DOUGH?

11. Idea for a new reality show? ○ No ○ Yes, _____.

12. Meet anyone new this week? ○ No ○ Yes, _____.

13. Caught a snowflake on your tongue? ○ Yes ○ No

14. States you've lived in? _____

15. Chicken tenders & ○ honey mustard ○ barbeque ○ other _____?

16. Spell well? ○ Yes ○ I'm average ○ No

17. IF U WERE INVITED TO A COSTUME BALL, WHO WOULD U GO AS? _____

18. ○ Green ○ Black olives ○ Neither, gross!

19. Sat on a rooftop? ○ Yes ○ No

20. FAVE THING TO SLURP THRU A STRAW? _____

Would you really want to be a queen?

1. First name (spelled backwards)? _____

2. Playing with a ○ kitten ○ puppy ○ guinea pig is the most fun.

3. WOULD YOU REALLY WANT TO BE A QUEEN? ○ ABSOLUTELY! ○ NO WAY!

4. Most expensive thing you've broken? _____

5. Nails on a chalkboard? ○ AHHH! ○ Doesn't bother me.

6. ○ Love(d) ○ Hate(d) dodgeball?

7. If u could teleport somewhere for 1 day, where would you go? _____

8. Wear/Wore braces? ○ Yes ○ No

9. Like to go barefoot ○ whenever I can ○ sometimes ○ never!

10. Most important thing about you? _____

11. EVER STEPPED ON A NAIL? ○ YES ○ NEVER

12. Look good in hats? ○ No ○ Yes ○ Eh, maybe a few.

13. Last game you won? _____

14. Last game you lost? _____

15. Double dipping is ○ so gross ○ not THAT big of a deal.

16. Ever had food poisoning? ○ Yes, from _____. ○ No

17. Something you've never tried? _____

18. Make any interesting sounds? __ No __Yes, I _____.

19. Popular song you love to hate? _____

20. Ever been hit by a ball? ○ No ○ Yes, I _____.

Absolutely!

Power

1. What do most people call you? _____

2. **Wear watch on your** ○ **right** ○ **left wrist?**

3. Can you go to bed hungry? ○ Yes ○ No, gotta have something.

4. Last craft you did? _____

5. Ever been in trouble for talking too much? ○ Yep ○ Nah

6. Ever been labeled "shy"? ○ Not hardly ○ A few times ○ Always!

7. Participated in a staring contest? ○ No ○ Yes. Did you win? ○ Yes ○ No

8. Fave kind of socks? _____

9. **Arm wrestled?** ○ **Yes** ○ **No**

10. Thumb wrestled? ○ Yes ○ No

11. "For real" wrestled? ○ No way ○ Uh, yeah

12. Best thing about the last day of school? _____

13. Worst thing about the last day of school? _____

14. **Know a lot of useless trivia?** ○ **Yes**   ○ **No, not really.**

15. Which color is scarier? ○ Red ○ Black

16. ○ Sweet ○ Sour pickles?

17. **BEST FRO-YO IN TOWN?** _____

18. Gone backstage at a concert? ○ No ○ Yes, I met _____.

19. ○ Corn on the cob ○ Loose corn niblets?

20. Fave Wii game? _____

BLUE

1. Name

2. What makes you blue?

3. Look good in blue? ● Yes ● No

4. Two blue things in your bedroom?

5. Someone you know with blue eyes?

6. Blueberry ● pancakes ● pie ● smoothie ● muffin?

7. ● Bluebirds ● Blue flowers?

8. ● Baby ● Navy ● Aqua blue?

9. Favorite blue jeans brand?

10. ● Fly the blue sky ● Sail the blue seas?

BLUE

11. Seen the ocean? ◯ No ◯ Yes, I've been to _____ .

12. ◯ *Little Mermaid* ◯ *Finding Nemo?*

13. ◯ Submarine ◯ Submarine sandwich?

14. ◯ Ocean bottom ◯ Outer space?

15. I would love to take a cruise to _____ .

16. Think SpongeBob will ever get his license? ◯ Yeah ◯ Nah

17. ◯ Crab legs ◯ Crabcake ◯ Krabby patties?

18. Owned a fish besides a goldfish? ◯ No ◯ Yes, a _____ .

19. Like calamari? ◯ Yum! ◯ Yuck! ◯ Whatamari?

20. Fave water activity?

unlimited ♡♡

unlimited possibilities...

1. Middle name? _____

2. IF U COULD GO BACK 24 HOURS, WHAT WOULD U CHANGE? _____

3. Buffets are ○ so much fun ○ germy and gross.

4. Last song you danced to? _____

5. MOVIE THEATER PREVIEWS ARE ○ANNOYING AND LONG ○EXCITING.

6. Coolest old person u know? _____

7. Had anything stolen? ○ No ○ Yes, my _____

8. Most difficult thing you've done? _____

9. Air ○ guitar ○ drums?

10. If u could change ur entire name to one letter, which would u choose? ☐

11. Tallest person you know? _____

12. Ever fainted? ○ No ○ Yes, I _____

13. Own a tiara? ○ No ○ Of course

14. ○ Chili ○ Veggie chili ○ Neither?

15. Old song you really like? _____

16. SHOOK OR KICKED A VENDING MACHINE? ○ YES ○ NO, IT'S DANGEROUS!

17. Something you love about where u live? _____

18. Something you can't stand about it? _____

19. Care what people think of u? ○ Yeah ○ Depends who it is ○ Nah

20. ○ Karate chopping Styrofoam ○ Popping bubble wrap is more fun!

1. Name? _____

2. Other names for you ur parents considered? _____

3. **What r u doing?** _____

4. What were u doing this time last year? _____

5. 2nd toe longer than your big toe? ○ Yes   ○ No

6. ○ Wal-Mart   ○ Target   ○ Other _____?

7. I was a ○ good   ○ mean   ○ hyper   ○ weird little kid.

8. **name of your very first teacher?** _____

9. Did your first teacher like you? ○ Yes   ○ No   ○ I don't remember

10. Pick change up off the ground? ○ Yes   ○ No

11. *Sleep with your bedroom door* ○ *open*   ○ *closed?*

12. ○ Love thunderstorms   ○ Lightning freaks me out!

13. ○ I don't want to get married.   ○ I would like to be married by age _____.

14. Crying in front of people ○ doesn't bother   ○ embarrasses me.

15. Fave symbol, logo, or icon? _____

16. Get motion sickness? ○ Yes   ○ No

17. ○ **Lemonade**   ○ **Pink lemonade?**

18. ○ M&M's   ○ Skittles?

19. Is your family "huggy"? ○ Yep!   ○ Not really

20. **FASTEST SPEED YOU'VE GONE AT IN A CAR?** [   ]

1. names you go by? _____

2. people who know you best? _____

3. sweets that go great together? _____

4. things you avoid? _____

5. objects in your backpack or bag? _____

6. things you've climbed? _____

7. places you've jumped from? _____

8. people or things that make u LOL? _____

9. things you've lost? _____

10. things that give u the creeps? _____

11. reasons that make u run fast? _____

12. things you wish existed? _____

13. foods you'd like to eat every day? _____

14. jobs you'd never do? _____

15. activities u do fast? _____

16. activities that take u forever? _____

17. reasons u stay awake @ night? _____

18. sticky things you love? _____

19. things u don't like to do in public? _____

20. things u don't like to do alone? _____

Write down another word, sentence, or really short story.

Name _____

noodles _____

bumblebees _____

HAUNTED HOUSE _____

flip-flops _____

paws _____

fist bump _____

yellow _____

fairy _____

fortune cookies _____

rock band _____

I have a doppelganger
my friends say she looks just like me
should I try to find her?

1. Your last name (in pig Latin)? _____

2. Have a doppelganger in town (person who looks like you)? ○ Yes ○ No

3. Worst thing you've ever found in your food? _____ in _____.

4. Most annoying fashion trend? _____

5. How do you feel about purple? _____

6. Are you a pouter? ○ Oh yeah ○ Sometimes ○ Nah

7. What makes you tense? _____

8. Coolest thing about your family? _____

9. Weirdest thing about your family? _____

10. Snort when you laugh? ○ Yes ○ Sometimes ○ No

11. Do you make up songs? ○ No ○ Yes R they any good? ○ Yes ○ No

12. Yummiest thing in your fridge right now? _____

13. Grossest thing in your fridge right now? _____

14. ○ **Talking** ○ **Texting on phone?**

15. What would be your superhero name? _____

16. Fave famous athlete? _____

17. How many monogrammed items do you own? _____

18. Best street food? ○ Hot dogs ○ Candied nuts ○ Crepes ○ Pretzels

19. What could you write a book about? _____

20. Most interesting person you've ever met? _____

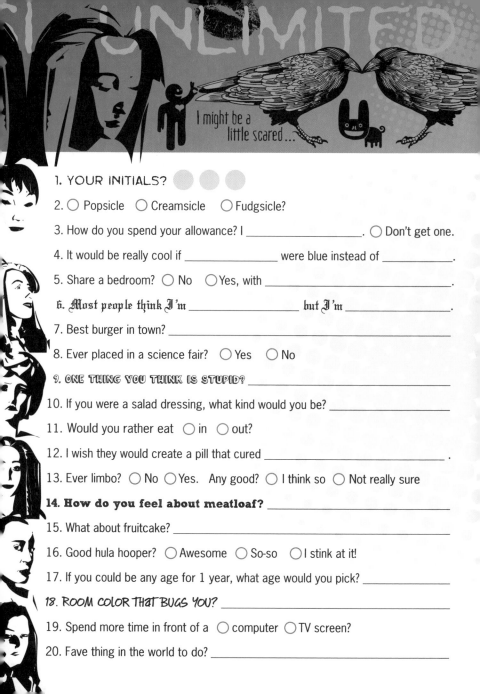

I might be a little scared...

1. YOUR INITIALS?

2. ◯ Popsicle ◯ Creamsicle ◯ Fudgsicle?

3. How do you spend your allowance? I _____. ◯ Don't get one.

4. It would be really cool if _____ were blue instead of _____.

5. Share a bedroom? ◯ No   ◯ Yes, with _____.

6. Most people think I'm _____ but I'm _____.

7. Best burger in town? _____

8. Ever placed in a science fair? ◯ Yes   ◯ No

9. ONE THING YOU THINK IS STUPID? _____

10. If you were a salad dressing, what kind would you be? _____

11. Would you rather eat ◯ in ◯ out?

12. I wish they would create a pill that cured _____ .

13. Ever limbo? ◯ No ◯ Yes. Any good? ◯ I think so ◯ Not really sure

14. **How do you feel about meatloaf?** _____

15. What about fruitcake? _____

16. Good hula hooper? ◯ Awesome   ◯ So-so   ◯ I stink at it!

17. If you could be any age for 1 year, what age would you pick? _____

18. ROOM COLOR THAT BUGS YOU? _____

19. Spend more time in front of a ◯ computer ◯ TV screen?

20. Fave thing in the world to do? _____

Name . . . .

1. First name with letters mixed up . . . .

2. ◯ Lime ◯ Lemon ◯ Lemon-lime?

3. Ever had a treehouse ? ◯ Yes ◯ No

4. Do u wear green? ◯ No ◯ Yes. Look good in it? ◯ Yes ◯ Dunno

5. Fave green veggie? . . . .

6. ◯ Chartreuse ◯ Grass green ◯ Forest green?

7. Talked with a parrot? ◯ No ◯ Yes. What did it say? . . . .

8. Ever golfed? ◯ No ◯ Just goofy golf ◯ Yes

9. Ever found a four-leaf clover? ◯ Yes ◯ No

10. Most green ($) you've had in your pocket? . . . .

11. Would you try green eggs and ham? ◯ Sure ◯ No way!

12. ◯ Spearmint ◯ Peppermint?

13. Believe in little green men? ◯ Yes! ◯ No, aliens don't exist.

14. Someone you know with green eyes? . . . .

15. Have any Irish in you? ◯ No ◯ Don't know ◯ Yes, ...

16. Like the movie with the Emerald City? ◯ Yes ◯ No, witch is scary!

17. Something that made you green with envy? . . . .

18. ◯ Green ◯ Red apples?

19. Write down the first green thing you see. . . . .

20. What 3 wishes would u ask of a leprechaun? . . . .

GET
AIR

UNLIMITED TRAVEL

Would you mind having wings
if it meant you could fly?

1. **First name upside down?** _____

2. Chew on the ends of pencils or pens? ○ Yes ○ No

3. Something you've done that ur friends haven't? _____

4. **What sound makes u laugh?** _____

5. Like hot sauce? ○ Luv it! ○ No

6. Last subject you Googled? _____

7. Something u want to know about the future? _____

8. Do/Did u have Barbie dolls? ○ No ○ Yes. Which kind? _____

9. What's on ur nightstand or next to ur bed? _____

10. **Something you quit?** _____

11. Have a fave Disney princess? ○ No ○ Yes, _____.

12. Want to go to college? ○ No ○ Yes. Where? _____

13. **What makes you sneeze?** _____

14. Taste the difference between Coke and Pepsi? ○ Absolutely ○ Not really

15. Fave soap scent? _____

16. Last thing you borrowed? _____

17. **Like Scrabble?** ○ Yes ○ No

18. How 'bout Monopoly? ○ Yes ○ No

19. If u could live 1 day of ur life over, which would u choose? _____

20. **COOLEST CAR YOU'VE BEEN IN?** _____

1. LAST NAME? _____

2. Ever swallowed a non-food item? ○ No ○ Yes, _____.

3. ○ **Speakers**   ○ **Headphones**   ○ **Ear buds?**

4. Last song you sang out loud? _____

5. Would u mind having wings if it meant u could fly? ○ No   ○ Yes

6. What do you put ketchup on? _____

7. HOW 'bOUT MUSTaRD? _____

8. Prefer to ○ take ○ be in a photograph?

9. Fave carnival game? _____

10. Tend to blame ○ yourself   ○ others   ○ a little of both?

11. Best part of a sandwich? _____

12. What's your current mood? _____

13. Fave four-legged creature? _____ Y? _____

14. ○ Fresh fruit   ○ Fruit-flavored candy?

15. Last fight I had was about _____

16. Sneakiest place you've ever hidden? _____

17. Would you like to be cloned? ○ **Oh yeah** ○ **No way**

18. Fave kind of cheese? _____

19. What does your mouse pad look like? _____

20. ○ **Daredevil** ○ **Scaredy pants?**

WOULD U RATHER

Name _____

have a spy ◯ camera ◯ listening device?

be ◯ respected for doing the right thing ◯ liked for being fun?

◯ work really hard and make millions ◯ win millions in a contest?

◯ sleep in a hammock every night ◯ sit in a wooden chair every day?

hang out ◯ 1 time with a really cool celebrity ◯ for a month with a guy you like?

always have ◯ a stain on your shirt ◯ something stuck in your front teeth?

have a lifetime of ◯ bad hair ◯ "I don't like any of my clothes!" days?

be a ◯ cat with a litter box ◯ dog that has to be taken out?

◯ have a cold for 6 months ◯ be cold for 6 months?

have the ability to ◯ breathe underwater ◯ go without sleep?

◯ make new friends each year ◯ keep your same friends you have now forever?

have ◯ 3 eyes ◯ 4 arms?

live without ◯ salt ◯ sugar?

have to wear ◯ jeans to work out ◯ a formal gown to the movie theater?

always have to wear cowboy ◯ boots ◯ hat?

Whatdoyouthinkof
when you see or hear these words ...

Write down another word, sentence or really short story.

Name

POPCORN _____

stars _____

winter _____

texting _____

pirate _____

ELEVATOR _____

castle _____

BOYS _____

furry _____

pebbles _____

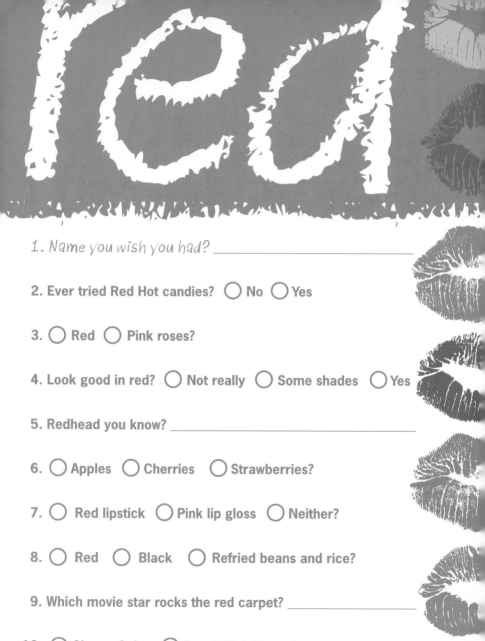

red

1. Name you wish you had? _____

2. Ever tried Red Hot candies? ◯ No ◯ Yes

3. ◯ Red ◯ Pink roses?

4. Look good in red? ◯ Not really ◯ Some shades ◯ Yes

5. Redhead you know? _____

6. ◯ Apples ◯ Cherries ◯ Strawberries?

7. ◯ Red lipstick ◯ Pink lip gloss ◯ Neither?

8. ◯ Red ◯ Black ◯ Refried beans and rice?

9. Which movie star rocks the red carpet? _____

10. ◯ Cherry Coke ◯ Pepsi Wild Cherry?

rouge
rojo
rosso

11. Which is cooler ... red ◯ dress ◯ shoes ◯ bag?

12. Something red you would not part with? _____

13. Fave character in ruby red slippers movie? _____

14. ◯ Red velvet ◯ Chocolate ◯ Vanilla cake?

15. Valentine's Day is ◯ so overrated ◯ OK, I guess ◯ so sweet.

16. How'd u get your last bad sunburn? _____

17. ◯ Red ◯ Black raspberries?

18. Turn red when you are really mad? ◯ YES! ◯ No

19. How 'bout when you're embarrassed? ◯ Oh yeah ◯ No

20. ◯ Tomato ◯ Cream sauce on pasta?

Ever seen a shooting star?

1. NICKNAME? _____

2. ○ Sunflower seeds ○ Peanuts ○ Granola?

3. Height? ☐ ☐

4. Shoe size? ☐

5. How long have you lived in the house you're in? _____

6. ○ Confetti ○ Silly string?

7. What do you say when someone sneezes? _____

8. Kind of cell phone u have or want? _____

9. Know what ur name means? ○ No ○ Yes, _____ .

10. Fave love song? _____

11. ○ Cheetos ○ Doritos ○ Fritos ○ Tostitos ○ None of them?

12. Question u would ask the President? _____

13. Comforter pattern & color? _____

14. Trait ur parents love about u? _____

15. Trait of yours that bugs ur parents? _____

16. ○ Rock wall   ○ Mountain climbing?

17. Something u always take with u when u leave the house? _____

18. What makes you fall asleep? _____

19. Oldest thing in your wardrobe? _____ from _____

20. Seen a shooting star? ○ Yes ○ No   Meteor shower? ○ Yes ○ No

1. First name without vowels? _____

2. 3-D movies ○ are really cool ○ make me dizzy.

3. Any exciting news to share? ○ Nope ○ Yep, _____.

4. Fave fair food? ○ Funnel cakes ○ Fried candy bar ○ Sausages ○ Shaved ice

5. I cheer myself up by _____

6. Graffiti is ○ a really cool art form ○ tacky ○ illegal!

7. Shove things under ur bed so ur room looks clean? ○ Oh yeah ○ Uh no

8. Unsolved mystery in ur life? ○ No ○ Yes, _____.

9. ○ Sit-down dinner ○ Eat on the run?

10. COOKIE(S) ○ aND MILK ○ aND CREAM ICE CREAM ○ DOUGH?

11. Idea for a new reality show? ○ No ○ Yes, _____.

12. Meet anyone new this week? ○ No ○ Yes, _____.

13. Caught a snowflake on your tongue? ○ Yes ○ No

14. States you've lived in? _____

15. Chicken tenders & ○ honey mustard ○ barbeque ○ other _____?

16. Spell well? ○ Yes ○ I'm average ○ No

17. if U were invited to a costume ball, who would U go as? _____

18. ○ Green ○ Black olives ○ Neither, gross!

19. Sat on a rooftop? ○ Yes ○ No

20. FAVE THING TO SLURP THRU A STRAW? _____

Would you really want to be a queen?

1. First name (spelled backwards)? _____

2. Playing with a ○ kitten ○ puppy ○ guinea pig is the most fun.

3. WOULD YOU REALLY WANT TO BE A QUEEN? ○ ABSOLUTELY! ○ NO WAY!

4. Most expensive thing you've broken? _____

5. Nails on a chalkboard? ○ AHHH! ○ Doesn't bother me.

6. ○ Love(d) ○ Hate(d) dodgeball?

7. If u could teleport somewhere for 1 day, where would you go? _____

8. Wear/Wore braces? ○ Yes ○ No

9. Like to go barefoot ○ whenever I can ○ sometimes ○ never!

10. Most important thing about you? _____

11. EVER STEPPED ON A NAIL? ○ YES ○ NEVER

12. Look good in hats? ○ No ○ Yes ○ Eh, maybe a few.

13. Last game you won? _____

14. Last game you lost? _____

15. Double dipping is ○ so gross ○ not THAT big of a deal.

16. Ever had food poisoning? ○ Yes, from _____. ○ No

17. Something you've never tried? _____

18. Make any interesting sounds? __ No __Yes, I _____.

19. Popular song you love to hate? _____

20. Ever been hit by a ball? ○ No ○ Yes, I _____.

Unlimit